TYKE TOWERS:
YORKSHIRE'S WINDMILLS

by

Alan Whitworth

Landy Publishing
2002

ISBN 1 872895 57 3
A catalogue record of this book is available from the British Library.
Layout by Mike Clarke. *Tel/Fax: 01254 395848*
Printed by Nayler the Printer Ltd., Accrington. *Tel: 01254 234247*

Alan Whitworth has also written or edited:
Exploring Churches
Yorkshire Windmills
Aspects of the Yorkshire Coast (2)
Aspects of York
Foul Deeds & Suspicious Deaths on the Yorkshire Coast

Landy Publishing have also published:

Bygone Bentham by Joseph Carr
A Century of Bentham by David Johnson
Bolland Forest & the Hodder Valley by Greenwood and Bolton
Landy Publishing have published many books relating to **Lancashire**. This is their first book bearing the word **Yorkshire** on the title page. Landy stands for **L and Y** which means **Lancashire and Yorkshire**.

A full list is available from:

Landy Publishing
'Acorns' 3 Staining Rise, Staining, Blackpool, FY3 0BU
Tel/Fax: 01253 895678

List of Contents

The Windmill

Henry Wadsworth Longfellow (1807-82)

Behold! a giant I am!
Aloft here in my tower,
With my granite jaws I devour
The maize, and the wheat, and the rye,
And grind them into flour

I look down over the farms;
In the fields of grain I see
The harvest that is to be,
And I fling to the air my arms,
For I know it is all for me.

I hear the sound of flails
Far off, from the threshing-floors
In barns, with their open doors,
And the wind, the wind in my sails,
Louder and louder roars.

I stand here in my place,
With my foot on the rock below,
And whichever way it may blow
I meet it face to face,
As a brave man meets his foe.

And while we wrestle and strive
My master, the miller, stands
And feeds me with his hands;
For he knows who makes him thrive,
Who makes him lord of lands.

On Sundays I take my rest;
Church-going bells begin
Their low melodious din;
I cross my arms on my breast,
And all is peace within.

An illustration of the two windmills at Doncaster Gate, Rotherham, from Christopher Thompson's *Hallamshire Scrapbook* published in 1827.

A painting of Sutton Mill in the 1930s by Karl Wood. Reproduced with permission from Lincolnshire Museums & Art Galleries Collection.

Introduction

Aureum Dei Donum Frutmentum Molinus —

We Grind the Corn, the Golden Gift of God

*September 1, **Feast of St Verana**, a Patron Saint of Millers*

Few structures add as much atmosphere to the English countryside as a windmill. Even in ruination, a mill possesses a dignity few other buildings can equal. The history of windmills stretches back far into antiquity, and while none of the first mills in the country survive, among the windmills which do remain to the present time are some that are at least three hundred years old, and many over a century in age.

Yorkshire today is perhaps not so well noted for windmills as other counties. Certainly in comparison with Norfolk, Suffolk and Lincolnshire, the county pales into insignificance; but in times past, stretching across the three Ridings, Yorkshire could hold its own for numbers. As we travel about it now, it is difficult to imagine a landscape populated every few miles with windmills, but so it was. Indeed, one authority writing in the September 1954 issue of the *Yorkshire Life*, suggested that approximately one windmill still existed *'every six miles over a wide area of the East Riding'*.

It is said that windmills were introduced in Britain by returning crusaders. Possibly this is true, as the earliest written reference to a windmill in England, dated 1185, relates to a mill at Weedley, in Yorkshire, let at a rental of eight shillings a year. At that time the windmill and manor of Weedley, a small sheep farming community located towards the end of the parish of South Cave in the East Riding, was owned by the Knights Templars. This was a militant religious order founded at the beginning of the tenth century in Outremer, an arid sandy region on the border of modern Iran and Afghanistan, which was noted for windmills as early as the ninth century — a coincidence which lends credibility to this supposition.

Originally windmills would have been built on the open fields or common land of the village. The erection of a mill was a privilege granted only to the lord of the manor or the Church, and with its ownership went certain rights in respect of milling corn, known as *Mill Soke*. Under this feudal custom, tenants of the manor were required to bring their corn to the manorial mill for grinding. The miller, often a tenant put in by the overlord, was allowed for his labour to retain a predetermined percentage of the flour he produced with the exception of that belonging to his lordship, who could have his corn ground free. It was the duty of the miller to collect the toll or *multer* as it was often known due to the owner, and present it at the manorial court either in money or in kind, on prescribed dates.

Failure to abide by and uphold this state of medieval Soke Law was a serious matter and, in 1573, William Plewman, a miller of York, was fined 13s 4d by the manorial court *for not attending the Court and for not bringing the Toll Dishe according to custom*.

Through this responsibility, the miller was often the recipient of much mistrust, and Chaucer in his epic *Canterbury Tales* drew attention to this aspect of his character, observing in *'The Millers Tale'*:

> *His was the master hand at stealing grain.*
> *He felt it with his thumb and thus he knew*
> *Its quality and took three times his due . . .*

Such acts were not without foundation, and in 1725 William Scutard, the miller of Thorne (Temple Newsam parish), was accused in his absence of falsely setting the stones *'in order to steal the flour of the customary tenants'*.

The earliest medieval windmills were so designed that they became known as *post mills*. Free-standing, the wooden-framed body of the mill was supported on a massive upright post which stood on a horizontal frame of two timbers crossed and jointed at right-angles. This arrangement of construction allowed the body of the mill to be rotated on the post in order to be faced into or away from the wind. This ensured as little interference to the milling process as possible during high winds or gentle breezes, whereupon the mill could be turned to better operate as desired.

Post mills were popular for many centuries, and if the site proved unsatisfactory, it was not uncommon for early windmills to be moved bodily to new locations to *better catch the wind*. One such, was that relocated by order of Abbot William Meaux from Beeforth to Skipsea, in Holderness, during the period 1372-96. Such action demonstrates the versatility of the post-mill over later static tower- and smock-mills built of stone or brick. These of course, could not be moved so easily, nor the sails be turned into the wind without a great deal of effort, and so often had to cease grinding during periods of either high winds or gentle breeze or calm.

Today, not one single instance of a post-mill exists in the county, and the only example anywhere near to Yorkshire is the finely restored windmill at Wrawby, near Brigg, just across the Humber Bridge, in Lincolnshire. However, up until 1961, the mill at Little Smeaton on the north bank of the River Went, some six miles south-east of Pontefract, stood as an excellent specimen of this type. Another survived at Hemingbrough, and an interesting windmill at South Skirlaugh shows how later developments enclosed the *post and cross-tree* in a roundhouse which was used as dry storage. Again, this arrangement could also be found at a mill in Burton Stone Lane, outside the city of York.

According to Roy Gregory in his book *East Riding Windmills*, it was the seventeenth century that first saw windmills employed for purposes other than grinding corn. It also appears likely that from midway through this century, windmills became more permanent structures than had previously been the case. Evidence indicates that it was not until the early-eighteenth century that the stone or brick tower-mill began to appear, in most instances as a replacement for an already existing post-mill. In some cases, however, the tower-mill was erected on a new and better site. Interestingly, while the first English tower-mill appeared in the fifteenth century, it is somewhat remarkable that this form of construction did not become common until three centuries later.

By far the largest concentration of windmills lies in the East Riding of Yorkshire. The flat landscape, with few fast-flowing streams, akin to that of adjacent Lincolnshire, Norfolk and Suffolk — counties steeped in a tradition of windmills — made the use of wind as a source of motive power a natural choice. Vast expanses of openness where the 'south-westerlies' could blow uninterrupted across the countryside, itself a rich agricultural plain yielding large quantities of grain necessary to feed the growing population of nineteenth century Britain.

It was the nineteenth century that became the *Golden Age* of windmills hereabouts; and the majority of surviving Yorkshire examples date from this period. The number of East Riding corn windmills for instance, increased from 71 to around 171 by 1855, but even this figure does not really illustrate the tremendous amount of mill construction that went on in the first two decades of the nineteenth century. Of the total of 171 windmills standing in that century, 29 were existing post-mills which had continued from previous centuries; 36 were tower-mills replacing earlier post-mills; 68 were tower-mills built on new sites; and six were windmills added to watermills. There were at least 18 corn-flour mills standing in Hull itself, but it is not clear which of these replaced post-mills.

One possible reason why there was such an increase in windmill construction in the nineteenth century might lay in the fact, that during the eighteenth century climatic conditions were responsible for the destruction of a large number of windmills. In many journals and diaries throughout that century, references are made to the ferocity of winds that swept across England. For instance, William Storr, of *Scalm Park*, in the parish of Wistow, near York, wrote the following which appeared in Wheater's *History of Sherburn and Cawood*, published in 1865, that is typical of numerous entries by other journalists:

In the year 1714-5 upon the first day of February was the greatest wind that had ever been seen in any mans time: it was at its highest betwixt 12 and 3 of the Clock, it blew down about half of the windmills in the Cuntrey [country], and there was blown downe a great number of barns, there was 8 blown down in Wistow & near 20 houses & barns at Selby; there were severall blown down which was but buelded the summer or 2 summers before; it did not leave one hay stack standing and at that time hay was very scarce for it followed A very dry summer; it took water out of the Rivers and Carried it in the Ayre [air] A very great way.

The distribution and construction of windmills reached its peak by the mid-nineteenth century, and by 1879 its prominence had began to wane. An East Riding directory for that year lists some 113 windmills (excluding the city of Hull). This number dropped to 104 by 1892; in 1897, the year of Queen Victoria's Diamond Jubilee, it had tumbled dramatically to 57 and reached 33 by 1909. In the year 1921 the figure for East Riding windmills had fallen to just eighteen!

During this time, many millers had installed steam engines, or had their windmills converted to electric power, two factos that more than any other, contributed to the demise of the windmill. In the East Riding, the last two mills to operate by wind were Preston's Mill, at Seaton Ross, dismantled in 1951, and Skidby Mill, where the use of wind-power was discontinued in 1954. Ironically, Skidby Mill in recent years has experienced a new lease of life due to a revival in interest in wind-power and in the study of these buildings — and today, it operates as the only working windmill in Yorkshire — having come full circle back to wind-power.

My interest in windmills reaches back well over ten years, and culminated in my book *Yorkshire Windmills* published in 1991. Now, ten years on, further research and losses have created a need for a new work on the subject. Obviously, with the production of any book, the research could not have been carried on without the assistance of others. As a consequence, I am indebted to the many owners who allowed me the opportunity to measure and photograph their mills and talk to me about their buildings. Also individuals who have assisted me with notes especially Michael G Fife, Honorary Secretary of the Poppleton History Society and to Mrs Barbara Howard whose family descendants the Nicholson's, include five generations of corn millers and was happy to share her family history with me. Also to the many who have written before on the subject, and in particular I should like to acknowledge the work of Roy Gregory and his volume *East Yorkshire Windmills* (1985). His enthusiasm and dedication to the research of windmills in this part of the county has made a major contribution to our knowledge and understanding of these buildings. Also the staff of various libraries and institutions for finding references and allowing the use of material, in particular Tony Munford, Archives and Local Studies Section, Rotherham Central Library.

Lastly, I should like to record my debt of gratitude to Professor Donald W Muggeridge and his father, without whose foresight in photographing windmills of Yorkshire at a period when great changes were occurring our archives would be the poorer, and who by correspondence has given permission for their use. These photographs are housed in the Templeman Library of the University of Kent, Canterbury, to who Mr Muggeridge made a donation of the glass negatives of his father and his own collection for posterity. This archive forms the basis of the book and unless otherwise stated, all the photographs are from the Muggeridge collection.

Finally, a word about the format of this work. My original book *Yorkshire Windmills* along with Roy Gregory's *East Yorkshire Windmills* are in essence text books. Even today, they both remain the best-published works on the subject, and are extremely detailed. Indeed, a reviewer of my *Yorkshire Windmills* in the prestigious *Yorkshire Archaeological Journal* wrote '... *the book is clearly a labour of love ... and the author has made a substantial investment of time and there is no doubt the reader can benefit from the wealth of references collected'*. The idea of this latest venture, however, is to illustrate the remaining windmills of Yorkshire without too much preamble, and where possible to revise errors and omissions in my earlier volume and add new information. However, it is not to be viewed as a scholarly book. For the serious student, I would refer them to the two titles mentioned — otherwise, this is first and foremost a pictorial celebration and record of these Tyke towers for the avid amateur historian and informed reader.

Alan Whitworth, Whitby, February 2002

Aberford (WY)

Aberford possessed two corn windmills both dating from the eighteenth century. One, situated near to the village itself, was named *Aberford Mill* and stood up Windmill Lane, which, like the mill itself was swept away by the construction of the A1(M) by-pass road. Built of local magnesium limestone, by 1963 it was described as a *sad ruin*. In 1822 the miller was Joseph Groves, however, by the late-nineteenth century it had ceased production altogether and the sails had been removed. Following this, the windmill fell into decay and was eventually demolished in 1984.

The second of Aberford's windmills, *Hicklam Mill*, lies on the edge of Hook Moor, three-quarters of a mile to the south of the village and still exists, visible from the A1(M) and may be connected with nearby *Hicklam House*. This too is built of magnesium limestone. Its date of erection is uncertain, however, it must have been put up by the mid-eighteenth century as there is an interesting story connected with it and a local Methodist preacher, Samuel Hick. He died at nearby Micklefield and is buried in Aberford churchyard.

One day in 1817 Sammy Hick was preaching at Knottingley. Finishing, he invited his listeners to a Love-feast at Micklefield, naming a future date and adding that he had two loads of corn that would be ground for the occasion. As the day of the feast drew nearer, so did a local flour shortage become more acute, for the windmills had been idle due to a lack of wind. This did not deter Sammy however, he took his corn to *Hicklam Mill* and instructed the miller to unfurl the sails and prepare to grind the corn.

The miller obliged and Sammy knelt in a corner of the mill and began to pray. As he rose from his prayers, the miller rushed in to the mill calling, *"The sails, they are turning." "The wind has been sent by Him who holds us all in His hands,"* was Sammy Hick's quiet reply. When the corn was ground the sails stopped. Others who had seen the windmill working had begun to flock with their corn but it was too late. Sammy had gone — and so had the wind!

In 1822 the miller of *Hicklam Mill* was Joseph Steel. Today the mill is under-going conversion to a house.

Aberford Mill in 1935. Today it has been converted to a house.

Hicklam Mill, Aberford (NY) in 1995. (Author's photo)

Appleton Roebuck (NY)

On Jeffery's *Map of Yorkshire* published in 1772, a windmill is shown here. Today, a ruined mill stands on an eminence a little to the west of the village, just off the road to Bolton Percy. This no doubt sits on the same site as the eighteenth century mill. The derelict mill, built of machined brick, stands four storeys high. However it is evident from the material that this structure only dates from the nineteenth century and therefore replaced, or was another mill, to that shown by Jeffery. Karl Wood the celebrated windmill artists painted a mill at Appleton Roebuck in August 1934 showing it as an empty shell. Internally, the mill measures 22 feet in diameter and has walls 19 inches thick. Some supporting beams exist in the upper levels with iron plates bolted on and a base plate of cast iron bolted to a squared stone 26 inches x 31 inches, on to which the main shaft of the windmill sat, still remains more or less in situ.

In 1822 the corn miller was Robert Denton.

The mill at Appleton Roebuck as it stands in 2001. (Author's photo)

Askham Bryan (NY)

At Askham Bryan, a tower is still very much in evidence today, situated on the same ridge of land as a number of other windmills. Exposed on a circular mound and constructed of ashlar masonry, a pressure-fed water tank was added to the top of the disused windmill shell at the end of the nineteenth century. The cement-rendered tank carries a fenestrated parapet and is out of alignment with the mill tower. From an aesthetic point of view, the piping connected with its use as a water tank is distracting — and one cannot but compare it with the mill tower at Bramham, where all the piping is hidden away — and effort which allows the tower to better preserve its essential profile.

The date of Askham Bryan mill is not known, but a windmill is shown on Jeffery's map of 1772, which was probably the mill that exists today, possibly replacing an earlier wooden post-mill.

The mill at Askham Bryan in 1992. (Author's photo)

Askham Richard (NY)

The windmill of Askham Richard, stood along Old Mill Lane, both of which eventually were swept away during the construction of the village by-pass in 1986-87. Little is known about this mill except that it was small in stature, and was in profile more cylindrical and tapered than many. It stood on the same ridge of land as the nearby windmill of Askham Bryan, with splendid views over the Vale of York.

The mill house to Askham Richard Mill had become the *Windmill Inn* by 1900, and later was renamed *Windmill House* when it ceased to be a drinking establishment. It too, was demolished in the road scheme at the time when the derelict windmill finally disappeared.

In 1822 the corn miller was John Gaterhill.

Askham Richard and Old Mill Lane, from Edmund Bogg's *Lower Wharfedale*, published in 1904.

Austerthorpe near Leeds (WY)

John Smeaton, the designer of the famous Eddystone Lighthouse, also built a five-sail windmill known as *Flint Mill* in 1774. This location in Leeds is uncertain, but thought to be the windmill at Austerthorpe, near Whitkirk, which stood back from the Leeds to Selby road, near to *Austerthorpe Lodge*, Smeaton's home.

This mill, constructed of brick, was no longer working by the beginning of the twentieth century, and was derelict in 1928, standing without sails or internal machinery. It was demolishes shortly after and the site now forms part of a school.

Smeaton carried out a number of investigations into windmill sail design and concluded that the most efficient sail plan, was one of five single sails. By efficient, however, Smeaton meant effective in terms of the best utilization of available wind power. Five sails, unfortunately, are not so convenient to the miller who preferred even-numbered sails, as if one was lost or broken by storm, by taking away the sail directly opposite the miller could keep operating, as the balanced sails would still turn. However, take away an uneven numbered sail, and the remaining sails would be out of balance and would not turn without risk of damage to the mill machinery.

Flint Mill, Austerthorpe was built by John Smeaton. It is seen here in ruins; from a drawing by B. R. Hammond.

Top right: The much reduced shell of Bainton Mill as it stands today in 2001. (Author's photo)

Bainton (EY)

Bainton had a windmill in 1279, *held of the king* and *worth by the year four pounds*. A windmill was recorded at Bainton throughout the fifteenth and sixteenth centuries. In 1818 Bainton obtained a new windmill, and this is no doubt the one which remains today, replacing an earlier post-mill.

Inside the derelict brick shell, which is only the stump of the nineteenth century mill, the floor timbers and other woodwork lay as it collapsed, and on some of the pieces can be found carpenter's marks suggesting that they may be reused wood from a previous mill here.

At the time *Bainton Mill* was newly erected in 1818, it had four patent sails, invented by William Cubitt in 1807 and an ogee-shaped cap with a fantail mechanism. Mr R Wilson, who was an engineer and millwright at Driffield from 1898 until 1911 remembers an incident concerning *Bainton Mill* and its wands.

"When I was about fifteen years old I was painting the main sails. My master always taught us to chock the brake wheel when painting or repairing the main sails, but on this occasion we were depending on the brake only. I had just got on to the sail from my ladder when a great gust of wind started the sails moving. I had to drop fifteen to twenty feet to the ground and watch my paint go round with the sail!"

Barrow near Wentworth (WY)

The windmill at Barrow, about half a mile north-west of Wentworth along Mill Lane, which still remains, was constructed from materials provided by the taking down of a windmill in nearby Wentworth village. The erection of Barrow mill was completed by 1793, and the total cost of the work was £382 9s $1\frac{1}{4}$d. Mill Lane, the road that led to the new windmill was also made at this date. A substantial house was built for the miller and his family a year later as testified in the Wentworth Accounts for 1794 which record *paid sundries for erecting a new dwelling house, barn and stable,*

The windmill at Barrow, near Wentworth, photographed in 1996 as an empty house. (Author's photo)

etc Contiguous to the new windmill and other expenses relating thereto … £313 14s 5d.

Several enclosed fields surrounding the new mill were transferred from neighbouring farms for the use of the miller John Pearson. In addition to his first rent of £40 for the lease of the new windmill for the year ending Michalemas 1794, he paid a further sum of £10 for half a year's lease from Martinmas 1793, for the homestead at the mill and several parcels of land. This John Pearson was the same miller who had previously been the lord's miller in Wentworth village (see Wentworth, Roundhouse).

John Pearson stayed at Barrow Mill until 1800, when William Nodder took possession, but he remained only two years, after which time a Benjamin Jackson, perhaps the same, or a relative of the miller who had once been at a previous mill in Wentworth, replaced him. By 1825, however, it is evident from notes and correspondence in the Wentworth Woodhouse Muniments that Joshua Jackson had charge of the windmill. Possibly he was the son of Benjamin Jackson, although Joshua's name did not replace that of Benjamin in Earl Fitzwilliam's Rental until 1833.

Considerable repairs to the windmill took place between 1828 and 1831, but from 1824 steam power had been introduced, when in that year the Earl paid half the costs with Joshua Jackson to erect a steam corn mill near the miller's house. In 1829 a Matthew Turton built a bone mill near this corn mill, for grinding bones into meal for use in agriculture. He also repaired the windmill, having possibly had use of it from Joshua.

Notwithstanding the amount of work carried out on Barrow windmill during the nineteenth century, by June 1835 the mill had ceased working. The Estate Accounts for the year June 1834 to the same month in the following year show that Earl Fitzwilliam paid his foreman mason, John Sykes, £135 1s 0d *for converting Joshua Jackson's windmill into two cottages* — thus ended several centuries of wind-powered corn milling in Wentworth village.

The old mill at Barwick-in Elmet as it appeared without sails in the early 1900s. (From the author's collection, source unknow).

Barwick-in-Elmet (WY)

At Barwick-in-Elmet, during the early part of the fourteenth century, William, son of Elias de Garforth, granted to William the Clerk, of Allerton, *a messuage in the vill of Barwick-in-Elmet, together with twelve acres of land in Schepenrode, and the windmill of Shippen.* John de Dynelay's *Inquisition Post Mortem* of 1367 records him as holding what were probably the same twelve acres and the windmill from the Masters of St Leonard's Hospital, at York.

The Bailiffs Account for the year 1418-19 includes details of repairs to a windmill at Barwick-in-Elmet, needless to say the total is incorrect:

100 gross 'bragges' [nails] for making firm the old wheel
100 'midelspykyngs' for the repair of a 'loucher'   *3d*
Wages of a carpenter choosing timber in the Wood of
  Seacroft and making thereof a new wheel and
  planing it in the same mill   *6s 8d*
Wages of a sawyer sawing timber   *1s 0d*
Wages of a waggoner carting the same wheel from
  Rothwell to the said mill   *1s 0d*
Wages of a man cutting ash trees in Osmerthyck for the
  making of gates   *2d*
Wages of a waggoner carting the timber to the mill, two
  journeys at 4d   *8d*
Wages of a carpenter making anew four gates   *2s 8d*
Wages of a carpenter repairing the roof, $1^1/_2$ days at $4^1/_2$ *$6^3/_4$ d*
Wages of a cooper   *8d*

Sum   *14s $^1/_2$ d*

A survey of 1424 shows the windmill was leased by the Duchy of Lancaster, the owner of Barwick-in-Elmet, to John Ellis for 30 shillings a year.

Barwick Mill, a fine tall brick-built structure was a ruin by the beginning of the twentieth century and taken down in the mid-1930s.

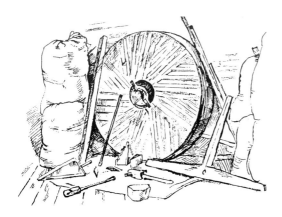

Top right: Derelict and falling into ruin, the shell of Beeford Mill in a farmyard will no doubt soon disappear completely. (Author's photo)

Beeford (EY)

A windmill was first mentioned at Beeford as early as 1372. This was a wood post-mill, and by the order of Abbot William Meaux, it was taken down and moved to Skipsea in Holderness during the period 1372-96. A *windmill with lands and the frank pledge there* was recorded in 1588.

There is no mention of a windmill on Jeffery's map of 1772, however, the village gained a new brick windmill in 1820. This probably replaced any earlier windmills that would most likely have been wooden post-mills. Undoubtedly the early-nineteenth century structure is the mill which survives to this day as a ruined shell.

Bempton (EY)

Today, the windmill at Bempton is converted into offices for a caravan company that now occupies the site. Built of brick, it stands five storeys high and dates probably from the nineteenth century when, in 1822, the miller was conspicuously absent from Baines *Directory of Yorkshire*.

This confusion is further exasperated throughout history when it is realized that at Buckton a windmill formed part of the Buckton family manor in 1314 and Bridlington Priory enjoyed the tithes of *Buckton Mill* in the early-sixteenth century. No more is known of its history, but a miller is still listed among the inhabitants in 1840. Confusion abounds whether an actual windmill existed, as the miller, a woman, is also listed under Bempton and indeed, the mill called *Buckton Mill*, was in fact, situated just over the boundary into Bempton parish. Bempton windmill, likewise, possibly erected in either the sixteenth or seventeenth century stands just into Sewerby, where mills are also separately recorded.

Interestingly, at nearby Sewerby, in 1619 a windmill stood in the fields of the township *nigh unto Bempton*, probably on a site close to the boundary with Bempton which had been occupied in the eighteenth century and later, by a windmill known as either Speeton or Bempton Mill.

Almost complete, Bempton windmill is today converted into an office. (Author's photo)

Beverley, Black Mill or Westwood Mill (EY)

Black Mill, today more commonly known as *Westwood Mill*, was begun in 1801 to the plan and estimation of Joseph Bateson, miller, to replace a previous wooden post-mill known as *Far Mill* that stood on the site as early as 1706. The work was completed by August 1803. Taller than most mills in Beverley, the tower measured fifty feet to the top and still survives in the keeping of the Borough Council.

When erected, *Black Mill* had four common sails, adjusted from a wide gallery running around the exterior. Later these were replaced by four patent sails, a gallows fantail was added, and the gallery was reduced in width. Measuring internally twenty-four feet at the base, it tapers to 13 feet 2 inches. Originally the exterior was whitewashed, but sometime afterwards the brickwork was tarred giving it the name *Black Mill*. The mill had two pairs of French stones and one pair of Peak stones for grinding different grains.

The mill was damaged by fire in the 1840s and repaired, to be partially dismantled in 1868 at the end of the lease, and was caught up in the squabbles over rights of pasture, when the machinery was removed and sold for £55.

Black Mill, also known as Westwood Mill, photographed in 1934 when it was a house. It survives today as a monument.

Crathorne's Mill about 1900, showing that by this time the free-standing windmill had been encased by other buildings. (Photo from the author's collection)

Beverley, Crathorne's Mill (EY)

Crathorne's Mill began life as a free-standing windmill of unusually large dimensions. It stood at least seven storeys high. Situated between the Beverley and Barmston Drain and the River Hull at the eastern end of Grovehill Road, it was first owned by Josiah Crathorne about 1830, and may have been known as *King's Mill* previously. A fire in 1858, said to be the result of a dust explosion, completely razed the building to the ground. Following rebuilding, it was fitted with a steam engine, but at what date it totally ceased to operate by wind power is not known.

In March 1868 while men were tarring *Crathorne's Mill*, the boiler in which the tar was being heated caught fire. This quickly spread to the newly applied tar on the tower exterior. The sails and fantail were soon alight, and as they fell they brought down the greater part of the outside gallery and wrecked the engine house. The damage was estimated at £1,600.

By the end of the nineteenth century the company had expended to such an extent that the windmill was almost completely encased by surrounding buildings.

Dogged by ill-luck, on 12 January 1907 another conflagration almost destroyed the premises. Crathorne's, however, struggled on, but the company appears to have ceased business soon afterwards.

Another view of Black Mill when it was being used as a house.

A pen and ink drawing of Butt Close Mill, later renamed Fishwick Mill, c. 1882 and probably by Caroline Brereton.

Beverley, Fishwick's Mill (EY)

In the nineteenth century, there existed ten windmills in Beverley (nine of which were corn mills) mostly situated on or adjoining the common known as *Westwood*. Originally this *Westwood* formed part of the manorial lands owned by the Archbishop of York over which the burgesses or freemen had the principal rights to graze animals. In the thirteenth century, this land was presented by the Archbishop to the Town Council subject to the continuation of the rights of freemen. This arrangement survived uncontested until 1835 in which year, through an Act of Parliament, changes brought about the introduction of new Councillor's onto the Town Council the results of which, led to an interesting and turbulent chapter in the history of windmilling in Beverley.

The first mention of what was to become known as *Fishwick's Mill*, occurs in Council Minutes dated 1 June 1761. It was then agreed to lease the northern half of *Butts Close*, a parcel of land on the eastern boundary of *Westwood*, to John Maud, of Sudcoates for 99 years at an annual rent of one pound sterling. As lessee, he was further given permission to erect a *windmill for grinding corn* and leave to dig chalk in the nearby pits *for raising the ground to an agreeable height whereon to erect the said mill*. However, this was subject to the condition that on quitting the premises at the end of the period, he was to demolish the windmill and leave bricks and tiles to the full value of twenty pounds. This windmill when complete was first known as *Butt Close Mill* and was a traditional post-mill.

In 1800 William and John Fishwick took the lease for a period of sixty years, the same conditions and restrictions being transferred, and the mill became known as *Fishwick's Mill*.

In the summer of 1861, the two Fishwick brothers carefully dismantled the windmill, left on site materials to the value stipulated and gave up possession of the mill house and outbuildings. A dispute then arose to who was entitled to take possession of these premises, the Town Council or the Freemen. In the end the Town Council felt that they had the right of ownership and took possession. At this point, the argument over the rights of pasturage on *Westwood* that had by this time being going on for some twenty-five years, often quite acrimoniously, erupted into open violence.

On Monday 2 September 1861, John Duffill spent the entire day touring Beverley urging all freemen to meet at the mill site. Meanwhile, *during the [same] day the members of the Property Committee [of the Town Council] visited the premises, and caused bills to be posted against the buildings, stating that any persons found trespassing would be prosecuted. Notwithstanding, at seven o'clock that evening, a large concourse of persons of all ages and both sexes* assembled and marched on the property, and after meeting only token resistance, tore down the mill house and outbuildings to the ground.

Outraged, the Town Council, after much debate, brought about prosecutions. Five key offenders were charged with riot and committed for trial, which at that time was a hanging offence. A week later a second group were prosecuted for the lesser crime of causing malicious damage.

Right: By 1935 the Union or Anti-Mill had become part of the facilities for Beverley Golf Club and was much reduced in height.

Beverley, Union Mill (EY)

In 1799 as in many other towns and villages, certain residents of Beverley formed themselves into a 'society' and erected a *Union Mill*. The foundation stone was laid with due pomp on 31 July 1800, by William Tuke, the son of Alderman Tuke who was an early benefactor of the scheme, providing a gift of ten guineas at the inception of the Union Mill Society. The windmill and outbuildings were completed by September 1803. On 6 August the following year, the Corporation granted a lease of the site to John Tuke, John Lockwood, and Thomas Duesbury, the Trustees of the Union Mill Society for a period of 99 years at an annual rent of one shilling.

Mercifully free of earlier town disputes, the *Union Mill* maintained a steady profit until about 1846, when there was a change of President, and the position was taken by John Hind. From then on a combination of factors affected the mill's production and profits, but undoubtedly mismanagement by Hind, was a major cause of its subsequent decline. As President and principal officer he held a position with wide powers of operation over a management committee with rather limited control over him.

Within six years it was in debt, and on occasions, the yearly dividend was not forthcoming, so precarious were its finances. In 1859 it was declared that a large amount was

Engraving of Union Mill, Beverley, by William Wynn, c. 1850.

required for repairs and improvements following severe storm damage and being struck by lightning. Following irregularities the accounts for 30 June 1862 show a direct order to pay the dividend of one penny per stone. These accounts appear to be the last published by the committee, and there can be no doubt that the mill's affairs by now were in something of a mess. The result of this state of affairs led to the dismissal of the miller, King Parker in October 1862, at which point all work at the mill seems to have ceased.

Following the death of King Parker on 17 December of that same year, and subsequent allegations by his family regarding outstanding money owed to him, a scandal was uncovered regarding John Hind, his abuse of powers and falsification of accounts. This led to two years of strife within the management committee. During this period milling was conducted intermittently, but in 1864 a serious attempt was made to clear outstanding debts and put the business on a sound footing. In 1871, Union Mill was let to Thomas Scruton at a rent of £45 per annum, with an arrangement that members should have an allowance of 1d per stone on all flour and offal purchased there.

Beverley Union Mill circa 1910. Often known as Anti-Mill, it was situated on the Common of Beverley known as Westwood.

Bishop Burton windmill photographed in 1935 after becoming a house, complete with crenelated parapet.

The currently empty windmill at Boroughbridge dates from 1822. (Author's photo)

Later, the mill was taken over by James Thirsk, recorded as miller in 1892, who produced his famous *Beverlac* flour there until 1897, when he ceased operation, soon after which, the mill was dismantled.

Today, the lower half of the tower remains, incorporated into the club-house of the Beverley & East Riding Golf Club. Some of the adjoining buildings connected with the mill also survived, but the mill-house was substantially rebuilt in 1912.

Bishop Burton (EY)

A Bishop Burton windmill was first noted in the year 1250, one of the earliest recorded in the county. In 1754, two millers were mentioned, one named Thomas Hopper. The mention of two millers undoubtedly indicates the continued existence of an earlier windmill whose presence was still evident in the late-eighteenth century. The two mills stood one at the north end of the village and the other to the south. *North Mill* was demolished by 1851.

The southern mill survived into the twentieth century, and after ceasing operation was converted into a dwelling. When complete and working, *South Mill* was extremely tall and the four patent sails were attended to via a wooden gallery around the mill at third-storey level.

Finally, it is said that a prominent mound in the village, is possibly the site of a former post-mill.

Bramham (NY)

Like Askham Richard, Bramham windmill stands on a circular mound, a feature common to many in order to add height to an otherwise small structure. Curiously, however, at Bramham, on the south side, a stone arch beneath it leads to a blocked-up doorway. No explanation exists as to its purpose, but it is conceivable that it was an entrance from the mill to this space which was most likely used as storage for milled flour or grain.

Built toward the end of the seventeenth century in magnesian limestone quarried locally, it is said that the sails were lost during a storm in 1829. For a period of 200 hundred years the Smith family were the millers. Interestingly, in 1822 three corn millers are named at Bramham, John Burnley; Michael Mande; and Joseph Scott. However, whether three windmills existed at that time is unknown. Since 1927 the tower shell, like Askham Richard, has been used as a water tank, first by Wetherby RDC and later by the Claro Water Board.

Boroughbridge windmill, July 1942,

Boroughbridge (NY)

A stone-built tower windmill, now derelict, remains on the outskirts of Boroughbridge and dates from 1822. Internally it measures 26 feet on the ground floor tapering to 14 feet 9 inches on the sixth storey. In the year of its erection Thomas Iles was corn miller. At what date it ceased operation is unknown.

In 1822 a public house in Boroughbridge was named *The Windmill* and may have marked the site of another earlier wind-powered mill in the town.

The remains of Bramham windmill from the south showing the curious underground storage facility. (Author's photo)

Burstwick (EY)

A windmill belonging to Burstwick Township, more properly known as Burstwick-cum-Skeckling, was mentioned from the thirteenth to the sixteenth centuries, and may have stood near *West Field* in Skeckling. Another windmill at Skeckling, was worked with a malting oven in 1772. Possibly it was this windmill that survived into the twentieth century. Built of brick and tarred to protect it from the weather, at first floor level an exterior gallery ran around the building.

Seen here in 1934, the windmill at Burton Pidsea is today a house.

The redundant windmill at Burstwick in 1934.

Burton Pidsea (EY)

There was a windmill mentioned at Burton Pidsea as early as 1275, undoubtedly a wooden post-mill with cloth sails stretched over a wood frame. In order to control the speed of the sails in the varying wind conditions, the material had to be reefed in the manner of ship's sails — often a hazardous task in high or stormy winds. However, failure to reduce the speed of the sails could often result in damage to the grinding mechanism.

In milling parlance, the sails of a windmill are known as *wands* or *sweeps*. Interestingly, sails stopped in a certain position would convey a message to the community. In the language of windmills, sweeps left like St Andrew's cross signified that the mill was shut for some time and the miller was away. Sails set in the form of St George's cross, indicated only a brief stoppage and the miller would soon return. Elsewhere, as in Holland, a windmill with the upper sail stopped before the vertical signified a celebration, while the upper sail past the vertical denoted mourning.

In 1834, a brick windmill was erected at Burton Pidsea, and this probably replaced the previously recorded wooden post-mill. Today, the remains of the brick mill are converted to a dwelling.

Cantley near Doncaster (WY)

The stump of Cantley windmill and its adjacent chimney, can be seen as you drive along the M18 between Branton and Cantley and the windmill is today associated with *Mill Farm*. The age of the mill is uncertain, but it appears on Greenwood's map of *Yorkshire* dated 1817, and the building also carries a datestone inscribed 'WC 1820', however, as this has been inserted into an existing opening, it may commemorate some refurbishment or change of ownership. The miller's at the time of Greenwood were James Brock in 1813. Thomas Hill a year later was still listed in William White's *Directory* of 1837 as corn miller at Cantley.

The tower mill, like the one surviving at Hatfield, is constructed of brick on a magnesian limestone base. The stump stands five storeys high, and measures 46 feet 6 inches to the existing top and approximately 23 feet across at the base internally, tapering to 11 feet across at the top. The brickwork is fourteen inches throughout. Several of the window openings have sandstone dressings and cills. At first-

The windmill at Cantley, near Doncaster, as it is today, with the chimney of the steam engine house towering up alongside. (Author's photo)

floor level there is a fireplace with a flue running up the inside wall. On top of the mill is a cast-iron curb of eight joined segments, each with nineteen integral teeth forming the gearing to move the cap.

Inside, remains of the milling gear still survived in 1993 and consisted of some bearings and supports, one pair of French burr millstones with stone spindle and iron bridging and the sack hoist drum. In about 1845 the windmill appears to have been converted to steam power and the engine drive entered the mill on the east side through a wall box, which can still be seen, and which carried the shaft bearing. While the windmill was powered by steam from the mid-nineteenth century, it is said that the sails were not actually removed until they were severely damaged in a gale about 1908.

It is thought that the windmill originally operated three pairs of stones on the second floor and that the surviving pair of stones on the first floor were probably steam driven. The chimney, bearing an inscribed stone and date 'WC 1845' is all that remains of the steam engine house that stood between the windmill and chimney to the east of the mill house. This is a very similar layout to that of Lelley windmill in the East Riding, which itself still remains with its adjacent chimney stack.

It is supposed that the initials 'WC', which can also be found on a barn in Chapel Lane, Branton, dated 1814, refer to William Carr, esquire, who owned the mill and barn in 1849. He was recorded as having ownership on Land Tax Returns of 1808 and 1834 and of three parcels of land, one being occupied by Thomas Hill. Later miller's of *Cantley Mill* have been Aaron Shaw circa 1850; Francis Lynas 1861-71 and John Holmes from about 1878 until 1923. The windmill finally ceased operations around 1927, when most of the machinery was removed.

Carleton near Pontefract (WY)

At Carleton, near Pontefract the remains of a windmill were converted into a house by 1959. This mill photographed sometime after 1930, is shown as a derelict brick tower mill. The empty shell is complete to the curb and stands at least five storeys in height. Greatly patched with brick near the top it appears to stand isolated in a rising open field and probably dates from the nineteenth century.

The remains of Carleton Mill sometime between 1930 and 1960.

Cherry Burton (EY)

The earliest record of a windmill at Cherry Burton is dated 1289. About the year 1295 the Prebendary of Dunnington owned a windmill here. These would no doubt be wooden post-mills and may have been the same mill structure.

There is no further mention of a windmill here, and the brick shell that survives today in the centre of a farmyard on the outskirts of the village, is probably of nineteenth century origin. Karl Wood overlooked painting it, and at what date it ceased operating I do not know, but it was certainly derelict and without sails in 1934 and photographs today show it practically unchanged in over sixty years.

Situated in a farmyard, the derelict shell of Cherry Burton windmill is used as a farm store. (Author's photo)

The empty shell of Clifford windmill near Tadcaster, shown in 1961, is no longer standing.

Clifford near Tadcaster (WY)

Old Mill Lane, Clifford crosses a parish boundary and leads to Windmill Hill upon which stands *Bramham Mill*, at that point in Bramham township, the road is known as Windmill Lane. New Mill Lane, Clifford leads a short distance to what was obviously an old water-mill that was enlarged in the nineteenth century, perhaps giving rise to its present title.

The site of Clifford windmill is now unclear, but it is probable from the architectural style, construction and materials that one existed in the eighteenth century, and survived into the twentieth century, photographed in 1961. However, today it has totally disappeared and its whereabouts is unknown but the illustration suggests a site on the village outskirts upon a rising eminence.

In 1822 Michael Maud was corn miller, but whether of the water-mill or windmill is unspecified.

Dunnington (EY)

A windmill stood at Dunnington in 1295, owned by the Prebendary there. This no doubt was a wooden post-mill. Following the mention of a windmill at this date, no other is recorded here until 1850, when a windmill stood near *Four Lane Ends*. The mill, however, was closed down by 1900, and derelict by the 1930s, when the photographer captured its use as an advertisement hoarding for an enterprising Tadcaster brewery.

East Cowick (WY)

Little is known about the mills of East Cowick or indeed, West Cowick. There is no record of any in ancient documents. However, a single windmill is shown on Jeffery's map of 1772 at East Cowick and another is marked at Turnbridge between Newlands and West Cowick. In 1822 two corn millers are named at East Cowick, William Conder and John Walker, suggesting that two windmills stood at that date. In West Cowick a separate corn miller named, William Nottingham, is recorded at the same time.

In 1932 Karl Wood painted the ruins of a mill at East Cowick, which was probably the remaining stump in a farmyard photographed in 1935.

The artistic remains of Dunnington windmill in 1935 when it carried an advert for the Tadcaster brewery John Smith's.

The stump of East Cowick Mill in 1935.

Ellerton (EY)

It is not known when the windmill at Ellerton was erected. There is no mention of any medieval mill here in ancient records. The surviving brick mill, which is today a house, is most likely of nineteenth century date. In 1822 the corn miller was John Brown.

Unusually, the mill at Ellerton was one of the few to have a wind-shaft mounted with a canister into which the sails fitted. In the East Riding a cast-iron cross was the

Ellerby (EY)

Ellerby Mill, sited near to the village railway station, is said to have been erected in 1830. However, a windmill here is marked on Jeffery's map of 1772. At what period this eighteenth century mill was rebuilt or simply disappeared, or if there were any earlier mills, there is no record, so it is unclear whether this nineteenth century mill stands on a previous foundation.

Photographed above in 1934, the sails had disappeared and it is possible that it last worked by electricity or steam.

Ellerton Mill in 1935 before being reduced in height and converted to a house.

preferred method of affixing sails and had its own distinctive shape. The sail arm was bolted onto the cross, whereas with the canister the arm was morticed into the arrangement.

By 1935 the tower mill was derelict, without sails, and was later reduced in size when converted to a dwelling sometime before the advent of the Second World War.

Ellerton windmill today after reduction in height and conversion to a house. (Author's photo)

Ferry Fryston (WY)

A windmill is mentioned at Ferry Fryston in 1247 in the Inquisition Post Mortem of Alice Haget. This site may be identified with the post medieval windmill on *Wentcliff Hill*. The later mill was constructed of magnesian limestone, but the whole tower has been much repaired with stone and brick and cemented over at one time. The upper one-sixth is built entirely of brick. Some of the oak beams that were part of the revolving cap, were taken down in the winter of 1961-2 others remain. Today the structure survives in a dilapidated condition as an animal shelter.

The windmill at Ferry Fryston was a derelict shell in 1934.

Fishlake (WY)

On Thomas Jeffery's *Map of Yorkshire* published in 1772 a windmill is shown at Fishlake west of the village. By 1932 two windmills existed here. At that date they were derelict and one was named *Nabb's Mill*, the other *North Mill*. It can be suggested that one dates from the eighteenth century and has the typical squat profile of that period, while the taller appears to date from the nineteenth century.

Both were built of brick and tar-rendered to protect them from the elements, but today, only one survives in a derelict state and is probably *Nabb's Mill*, the shorter of the windmills.

North Mill is probably 19th century and is seen here in 1934.

Nabb's Mill, which may date from the 18th century, photographed in 1934. Today it is converted to a house.

Garton, near Withernsea (EY)

Garton windmill, now derelict, stands isolated in a field on the outskirts of the village. The date of building is unclear but likely to be between 1824, where it is not shown on the Ordnance Survey map of that date, and 1840 when a miller is first mentioned in local directories.

Quite small in stature, it measures approximately 35 feet to the top of the brickwork at a point where the curb is missing, and inside at ground floor level measures 15 feet 3 inches across. A single pair of French stones and a pair of Peak stones remain, each four feet in diameter.

Internally, almost all the machinery survives intact, with very little damage, and almost all of it is constructed of timber, some geared cogs included. One feature of interest is a bevel cog in operation with a second bevel cog mounted on a horizontal shaft that passes through the wall of the tower to an external belt pulley to enable machinery, such as power saws, to be driven outside the mill.

Garton windmill standing alone in a field and showing the external belt pulley to drive machinery outside the mill. (Author's photo)

Goole, Shuffleton Mill, Hook Road (EY)

The life of the early miller was often a solitary one. Sometimes unsociable too. When the wind blew he had to arise and attend to the milling — whether day or night. In one such case, the nocturnal behaviour of the miller led his wife to demand that her husband erect an external ladder from the bedroom in order that he may leave the house without clattering down the main staircase and waking the entire household!

A miller's life was not without further troubles, litigation, bankruptcy — even death — were a common occurrence. In this respect, one wonders who handled the estate of William Greenfield, miller of Goole. He died in November 1840 when, as reported in the *Hull Advertiser*, after *endeavouring to stop his windmill, by taking hold of the sail, a practice too common after the brake is put on, he was taken up a considerable height from the ground and was thrown some distance from the mill. His back was much injured by the fall so that, after lingering, in great pain, until Tuesday morning, he expired, leaving a widow and several children to deplore the loss.*

Shuffleton Mill is today converted into a charming house. (Author's photo)

Hatfield, Ling's Mill (WY)

An early windmill was mentioned at Hatfield, which in the eighteenth year of the reign of King Edward II (1320-21), was let at an annual rent of eight shillings. This was a manorial mill and in the same accounts is an item of 13s 0d paid out each year *for ye wind mylne*, however, no explanation exists for this payment. Two windmills were mentioned in 1606, one sited at West Hatfield. There was a further mention of a windmill in 1608 which was noted in a grant dated 24 May from King Charles I to Cornelius Vermuyden, worth 13s 4d per year in rent, and which was previously in the ownership of Edward Ferrers and Francis Phipps, esquire.

In 1337 John, son of Peter de Stainford rented $31^{1}/_{2}$ acres of corn land in Thorne and Hatfield from John de Warrene, Earl of Surrey, for a rent of 10s 6d per annum. He was allowed to *make a way for his carriage to the mill of the said Count*, but it is not clear whether this reference is to a windmill in Hatfield or to one at Thorne, where at one time six windmills existed.

Mill-ways were an important consideration in the siting of mills. They would have to have had free access along their entire length, with no obstacles such as stiles, particularly where the route formed the only mean of approach to an isolated windmill. This was necessary to enable the manorial tenants to transport their grain to the mill and flour back again. The most common form of transport was the horse or mule, consequently, a mill-way would have to at least have had the width and substance of today's bridleway.

By 1771 *Ling's Mill* existed, a four storey brick mill which was rebuilt in the nineteenth century, and which in 1977, still showed signs of rendering. Later the building was demolished and all traces have disappeared.

In 1822 Baines mentioned two corn millers at Hatfield, John Cogan and John Rooley.

The majestic ruin of Ling's Mill, Hatfield, in 1934 before demolition.

Hatfield, Moss Croft Lane (WY)

Standing tall above Moss Croft Lane, on the edge of Hatfield village, the windmill forms part of the property now known as *Tower House*. Shown on Jeffery's map of 1772, the ground floor is composed of magnesian limestone laid as coarse rubble, while the remaining four storeys are built of brick, illustrating that at some later date, the windmill was rebuilt and heightened. The mill stands in its entirety and has a brick dentil course, no doubt added when the crenellations were formed after 1932 when the windmill had ceased to operate.

It should also be noted that the tall chimney shown behind the mill structure is now gone. This no doubt was the chimney to the steam engine shed, erected to supplement wind power at a later date. Or, as in the case of others mills, it may have been part of a drying kiln.

Today, the windmill shell, devoid of any internal mechanism, is used as a store. It is a Grade II listed monument and is one of six remaining windmills in the Doncaster MBC district.

Hemingbrough windmill was a wooden post-mill that survived until 1913. (Photo from the author's collection)

The windmill at Hatfield, Moss Croft Lane, above as it was in 1934.

Today, left, it remains almost complete in the garden of **Tower House**, the former mill house. It is used for storage. (Author's photo)

Hemingbrough near Selby (EY)

A windmill at Heminbrough existed in 1276 and repairs to it were frequently recorded throughout the Middle Ages. This mill was granted away by the Crown separately from the manor in 1609 and survived into the eighteenth century. The freehold was purchased by the Howden family in 1730, who often had tenancy of it previously. A mill is shown on Jeffery's map of 1772, and this is no doubt the one that stood between 1609 and 1913 which was a wooden post-mill.

An unusual feature of the mill at Hemingbrough was that the neck bearing — the semi-circular bearing which supported the wind-shaft immediately behind the sails — which was made of basaltic rock whereas the most common material was wood, particularly in post-mills. Another unusual feature, was that the wind-shaft was fitted with a canister into which the sails were morticed, where the more usual East Riding arrangement was to bolt the sails to a cast-iron cross that had its own unique shape.

In 1822 the corn miller was John Howdle.

Hinderwell Mill from Back Lane, which runs south of the village, and showing the steam engine house and chimney added about 1870. (Picture from the author's collection)

Hinderwell, Royal George Mill (NY)

Known as the *Royal George Mill*, the windmill at Hinderwell up the East Coast from Whitby, stood until the middle of the twentieth century, and possibly had its origins in the eighteenth century. The exact date of the first mill is not known, but local tradition has it that this mill was erected in 1820 and it may be the name came from a sense of royal pride following the coronation of King George IV in that year. An inscribed stone on the side of the building records that it was erected by Isaac Moon, who was also the miller at nearby Dalehouse water-mill, mentioned in Baines 1822 *Directory* as miller and farmer. When Isaac died in 1842, he left his entire estate including the windmill to his son, George Moon.

Standing seven storeys high, it was powered by four sails and contained two pairs of French stones and cylinders.

During the 1860s in an effort to improve business perhaps, consideration was given to forming the mill into a co-operative or union mill, and shares in the windmill were offered for sale. A notice was duly posted in the *Whitby Gazette* that read:

It having been considered by many persons desirable to convert the above property into a Union Mill in £5 shares a Meeting will be held at the Shoulder of Mutton Inn, Hinderwell, on Tuesday, 3 November 1868 at 6 o'clock in the evening when all are respectfully invited to attend. The utility of these mills is now generally admitted to be a great benefit to every neighbourhood where they are established, as well as a useful and safe investment.

Whether the *Royal George Mill* ever became a Union Mill is not known. Shortly after 1870 a steam engine was installed to help power the mill and in January 1873 it was mentioned in a conveyance, described as a *Wind Corn Mill with Steam Mill* and having *two granaries*.

It ceased production sometime toward the very end of the nineteenth century, with the machinery removed about 1915.

A former Hinderwell resident, Mr John Sanderson recalls his late aunt, Mrs Lyth, used to tell how the village held dances on the floor of the old windmill, and one very windy night they had just left for home when the sails of the mill fell to the ground, and they all had a fortunate escape.

Hornsea windmill at the time it had four common sails and ground corn.

Hornsea (EY)

A wooden post-mill existed at Hornsea, which was replaced by a brick tower mill in 1820. A windmill during the nineteenth century was associated with the site of Hornsea Pottery. This was a large five-sail mill. Earlier the site had been occupied by a brickworks, and it is thought that the windmill was used to power the machinery. However, inspection of a photograph of the five-sail mill and the windmill illustrated shows the two mills to be the same. At what date therefore the windmill ceased to grind corn is not known.

In 1822 William Amers was the corn miller and also kept the *Prince of Wales Inn*. By 1935 the mill had been converted into a house and appeared in a painting by Karl Wood.

Hull (EY)

Little is known about the very early windmills of the City of Kingston-upon-Hull. Gillet and MacMahon wrote of them, *when the king first acquired the town he had yet another windmill*, suggesting that they were numerous. This new mill acquired by the Crown was leased to Thomas Baron, rector of Kirk Ella. Like all buildings of timber at that period, it would have been easy to dismantle and reassemble in a different location, and it was agreed to allow the rector to move the mill, but *by 1312 the windmill on its new site was beyond repair. Nevertheless, around 1300 there were still more windmills than the inhabitants required and some must have existed solely to serve the needs of the mariners of the port.*

Another windmill was mentioned in 1349, and there was a mill on the west side of the town where there was frequent flooding, so much so, that a raised causeway known as the *wayour* was constructed in the mid-fifteenth century. This windmill, in the same vicinity, probably could not be approached except by the wayour, or later, by a bridge. By 1430 *several windmills stood round the town*. These were undoubtedly those that stood in Hull Street, near the North

Today the site of Albert Dock, this 1770 view of the Humber's west bank shows a windmill. Note the great tail pole at the back which the miller would use to turn the cap.

Gate and a map of great antiquity shows three outside the *Beverley Gate*. In 1536, during the Lincolnshire Rising these windmills at *Beverley Gate* were pulled down on 15 October.

Windmills were frequently mentioned throughout the sixteenth century and it is recorded that during the Civil War years 1641 and 1642 *some windmills were burnt down*. Only four windmills are shown on Jeffery's map of 1772, but by the nineteenth century the demand for corn had grown to such proportions, that mills were being erected at a tremendous rate.

In 1787 a new windmill was erected, and in 1795 the *Anti-Mill* was built by a co-operative and said to be the largest windmill in England. This stood in a yard between Balfour Road and Arundel Street on the South side of Holderness Road until about 1975.

A mill in Dansom Lane, but not the *Subscription Mill*, had the distinction of being the first windmill in the city to have steam power introduced. This mill standing seven storeys high had five double patent sails. Another mill with six sails was sited along the Holderness Road. In the 1820s a windmill that lasted only a few years was put up in Cent-per-Cent Street, described as *a good compact little corn mill*. It had five self-regulating sails and one pair of stones, and this was the only known example of a wooden smock-mill in the area, a type more common to the south-east of England.

Hull, Eyres Mill, Holderness Road(EY)

The first mill in Hull to be occupied by the Rank family was on Holderness Road. John Rank first took possession about 1841 and relinquished it in 1846 for a more suitable windmill in Southcoates Lane. This was John Rank's third mill, and at that period there were no less than ten corn windmills on the Holderness Road. The mill that he had taken was known as *Eyre's Mill*, erected in the eighteenth century, and is the only one of the numerous windmills in Hull to survive to this day.

In 1851, James Rank, who with his brother William had assisted his father John at the Southcoates Lane Mill, married at the age of twenty-two. John Rank handed over *Southcoates Mill* to his eldest son James, and once more took the mill in Holderness, his fourth and last move. And it was here, in the adjacent mill house of his grandfather that the most famous name associated with Rank, Joseph, was born in 1854.

In 1857 John Rank retired, and his second son took over the Holderness Road Mill. Here, William appears to have run in difficulties and had to borrow from his brother James *£70 for half profits in his business*. Notwithstanding making a profit in the following year, William was unable to make ends meet at the mill, and emigrated to Australia. The windmill then passed out of the hands of the Rank family who by this time were established in business elsewhere in Hull.

Today *Eyre's Mill* remains almost complete as a feature along Holderness Road in the car park of the *Mill Inn*. It retains sails, caps, fantail and much external gearing, and bears a blue plaque announcing that *'in nearby cottages Joseph Rank was born'*.

Eyre's Mill, on the Holderness Road, which John Rank took over about 1841. (From the author's collection)

Hull, Subscription Mill (EY)

The Directories of 1858 listed a total of eighteen corn millers in Hull, doubtless most the proprietors of windmills. In 1869 the *Eastern Counties Herald* reported *no part of the town was very far from the country and the view along the Holderness Road from Holderness House showed seven windmills in the town [of Hull] — and there were many more.* No doubt one of these was the *Subscription Mill*, whose foundation stone was laid in the year 1800 and which opened on 1 July 1801.

The *Subscription Mill*, owned by the Hull Subscription Mill Society stood in Dansom Lane. William Osborne laid the foundation stone and gave ten guineas toward the costs, Sir Samuel Standidge gave five guineas and Samuel Thornton, MP gave fifty. This windmill with its four patent sails, was one of the tallest in the county.

The *Subscription Mill*, was one of a number of 'Union' mills such as existed at Bridlington, Beverley, Whitby and elsewhere, formed by co-operatives in order to break the monopoly which existed toward the end of the eighteenth century forcing up the price of bread.

At the end of September 1800, all the windmills in Hull were stopped by several windless days and it was feared a shortage of flour would start riots such has had occurred in other parts of the country. When a wind came on the Saturday evening grinding went on all night and bread was immediately baked and sold on the Sunday, although a recent law passed required all bread to be twenty-four hours old before being offered for sale.

During the construction of the *Hull Subscription Mill*, a number of accidents occurred. In 1801, millwrights were horrified when the cast-iron axle tree gave way, as a result of which, one of the sails plummeted through the roof and floors of the adjoining millhouse and

Two recent views of Eyre's Mill in the car park of the *Mill Inn*, Holderness Road. (Author's photo)

34

A member's pass card for use by the Hull Subscription Mill Society.

Hutton Cranswick (EY)

Within a six-mile radius of Driffield are the remains of four windmills. The most complete of these is at Hutton Cranswick, where only the cap and sails have been removed. The brick tower is relatively slender and rises four storeys before the collar — two courses of brickwork — project to mark the division between the accommo-dation and the octagonal neck on which the cap and sails would have been mounted. Internally, much of the machinery remains.

It is not known when Hutton Cranswick windmill was built, but it is probable that it dates from the eighteenth century.

In 1822 the corn miller was Thomas Dawson.

embedded itself several feet deep in the earth, retaining an upright position. Fortunately, the two millwrights working on the mill avoided injury by jumping from the scaffold.

Somewhat carelessly, a few weeks later an apprentice engaged on the same mill endeavouring to let himself down from the gallery by rope, had less luck than the two previous. Unfortunately he did not secure the rope properly, with the result that it gave way. It was reported that *he fell to the ground with such force that he broke a leg and dislocated the ankle of the other*.

The Hull Subscription mill in its early years was associated with the Rank family, but what the precise connection is unclear. An old *Wheat Purchase Book*, bound in vellum, and kept from the year 1818 by Joseph Rank's grandfather, John Rank, has the words *Hull Subscription Mill* written on the inside cover. There are also references to certain monies paid to 'The President'. Possibly John Rank was foreman or agent of the Subscription Mill until he was able to acquire a mill of his own.

Now redundant, the windmill at Hutton Cranwick still contains much of its original machinery and awaits restoration. (Author's photo)

Keyingham, New Mill (EY)

New Mill, at Keyingham is one of two mills to survive here. Standing east of the village on the Ottringham road, it was erected between 1811 and 1825, and was last operated around 1900. A number of windmills stood in the village however, and another mill, mentioned in 1722 may have stood immediately north-east of Keyingham and possibly survived until 1760, when a windmill was shown on either side of the township.

Whichever this surviving mill is, it was in time converted to a residence, but none of the adjacent mill structures, such as the mill house survived with it. However, two of the millstones have been incorporated into the stylish gateposts that mark the entrance to the property. These show clearly how millstones were made up of stone fragments bound together, at which point the distinctive grooves — known as *cracking* — were chiselled into the surface of the millstone in patterns named *drill*, *feathering* or *stitching*.

Known as 'New Mill', today the windmill remains form part of a recently built dwelling. (Author's photo)

The remains of two millstones here form an attractive gatepost. Made from French Burr Stone, they show how they were assembled from smaller pieces. (Author's photo)

Keyingham, Old Mill (EY)

Keyingham *Old Mill*, dating from 1800, was first mentioned in the thirteenth century and again in 1620. Standing in *West Field*, north-west of the church. It was advertised for sale in December 1813 as a brick corn windmill with three pairs of stones and a new well-built house and about half an acre of land. Another advertisement in the summer of 1881 describes it as *a corn windmill with granary, warehouse, stables and newly created dwelling-house*. The mill house of 1813 has since been demolished, but the later dwelling-house remains.

The windmill tower stands just over forty feet to the curb, and has all the indications of having been built in two stages, as the angle of taper changes from the second storey upwards quite markedly. The ground floor has an internal diameter of twenty feet. When last powered by wind, around 1910, the mill had a typical Lincolnshire cap, four double patent

The Old Mill remains empty and contains much of its original machinery. (Author's photo)

sails, and a gallows fantail. A steam engine had been added to the windmill by this date, situated in a newly-built engine house. This was later replaced by an oil-powered engine that continued in use until electricity was introduced into the village, around 1932, when an electric motor was mounted inside the tower.

The sails and cap were removed about 1911 and the mill ceased operating about 1940. Today, the mill still stands almost as it was when it shut down.

Kilham windmill today forms part of a house. (Author's photo)

Kilham (EY)

At Kilham, west of Burton Agnes, a windmill was recorded in 1362, when it was said to be the manorial mill. This was last mentioned in 1694. In 1809, a windmill was built south of the village, in *Mill Back Side*. Eighty years later, however, steam had supplemented wind and by 1937 oil-power had superceded steam. Notwithstanding, in the following year the mill was derelict when Karl Wood painted it. Today the remains of the windmill form part of a substantial house.

Killamarsh near Cawthorne (WY)

On Jeffery's map of 1772 a corn windmill is shown at Raw Green, and a mill known as *Killamarsh Mill* stood to the west of Cawthorne village and south of *Cannon Hall* near to the present farm of the same name. A number of millers in the eighteenth century are associated with these mills but it is not clear which named mill is the *Killamarsh Mill* as it no doubt had a previous title.

In 1798 the Land Tax lists John Johnson at *Jowett House Mill* and the windmill at Clough Green and Joshua Armitage at the Nether Water Corn-mill and nearby windmill. In Cawthorne churchyard is the tombstone of William Kidd, of *Cawthorne Low Mill*, who died in May 1859.

Mention might be made of the windmill at nearby Higham, erected by John Stanley about 1747. Two years later the mill at Higham Common was sold to William Spencer, of *Cannon Hall*, for the sum of £72. Earlier leases of this windmill had allowed for its removal to another site, but it is uncertain whether Spencer attempted this. However, his journals record the payment of £20 12s 6d in 1749 for repairing the roof and sails, buying sail cloths and installing new gearing, almost half the money spent on *workmanship*, interpreted as labour costs.

The windmill at Killamarsh stood on an eminence overlooking *Cannon Hall* and was a brick tower mill that was later cement rendered. Three or four storeys in height, it had a massive tail pole which turned the cap and sails. It was demolished sometime in the 1840s.

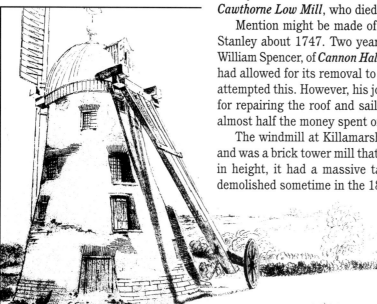

Killamarsh Mill, overlooking Cannon Hall, near Cawthorne, drawn by John Nattes c. 1807.

Kippax near Leeds (WY)

At Kippax, about a mile to the east of the village, adjacent to the old Roman road that connected Castleford with Tadcaster and Wetherby, stands in a farmyard the remains of an old windmill. This tower is squat in shape and built of magnesian limestone and carries a narrow band of brickwork at the top of its four storeys. This may not be original and only added when a flat roof was put on following the removal of the cap. The date of its erection is not known, nor when it ceased operating, but it was derelict by November 1932 when Karl Wood painted it.

In 1822 the corn miller was Benjamin Boggett.

Today Kippax windmill is a farm storehouse. (Author's photo)

Kirkbymoorside (NY)

At Kirkbymoorside, almost invisible yet practically in the town centre stands a windmill, today converted into a dwelling. Dating from 1839, a stone plaque records this fact and is further inscribed with the miller's name *G Rivis* and the builder's *W & J Spencley*. Today sporting a domed cap it stands five storeys high. Internally, the ground floor measures 20 feet in diameter while the upper fifth floor is 12 feet 5 inches in diameter. Constructed of red brick, originally it had a pitched roof as unusually, this windmill never had any sails! When completed it was found that any sails would encroach on the adjoining property's 'air space', as a consequence, it was only ever powered by a petrol and paraffin engine!

Situated in the town centre, the windmill has been converted into a house, yet is hardly visible from the street, hidden as it is by surrounding houses. (Author's photo)

The mill at Langtoft today is converted to a home. The adjacent mill house is now a restaurant. (Author's photo)

Langtoft (EY)

There was a mill at Langtoft in 1300 but it is not clear whether it was wind- or water- powered. No further evidence of a mill is recorded until a windmill was mentioned in 1712. This may have been the windmill stood about three-quarters of a mile north of the village beside the Butterwick road in 1854, which was described in 1865 as *an old post-mill* and subsequently replaced by a brick tower mill. A miller was last recorded as operating in 1925.

In 1938 the celebrated windmill artist Karl Wood recorded the mill without sails, but still relatively intact. The stump of the tower measuring 20 feet in diameter internally at the base remained in 1970. This was subsequently converted into a residence that survives and incorporates the original mill entrance as a window feature. Today the adjacent mill house is a restaurant.

Leeds, Colton Mill (WY)

At Colton, a windmill was recorded in 1249 the rent of which was given as 4s 5$\frac{1}{2}$d. This mill was in operation until the nineteenth century, and was last mentioned in 1963, when it was described as ruinous. Low and squat in shape, the bottom one-third was built of stone and the rest of brick showing that it had obviously been rebuilt and heightened at some later period. It was topped with a conical, slated cap at that date. Converted to steam power in the early years of the nineteenth century, when a steam engine shed was built adjacent with a square chimney, it was later reconverted to gas power. The mill and chimney was sketched in 1917 by J Steel.

Known as *Colton Mill*, the windmill was erected sometime in the eighteenth century and obviously rebuilt or enlarged in the following century. It stood in Bullerthorpe Lane, on the opposite side of the road to the site of *Austerthorpe Mill*, but was actually situated in the parish of Swillington, and may have been the mill drawn by Karl Wood in November 1932 on Colton Moor, shown as derelict without cap or sails.

The old mill on Bullerthorpe Lane, Leeds. Known as Colton Mill, it is now demolished. (From a drawing in the author's collection)

Leeds, Seacroft (WY)

Built of magnesium limestone in the eighteenth century, the windmill at Seacroft on what was Whin Moor, was marked on a tithe map of 1834 when the owner was stated to be John Wilson, who leased it to James Pearson. It was still in use in 1928, but not powered by wind.

For many years during the 1930s it was known as *Betty Barker's Mill*, taking its name from the owner or tenant of the farm in which it formed a part. In some documents, however, it is recorded as *Whin Moor Mill*. Today the windmill remains are incorporated into a hotel erected about 1967.

At the junction of York Road and the Leeds Ring Road, Whin Moor Mill now forms part of a hotel. (Author's photo)

Seacroft or 'Betty Barker's' Mill in 1942.

Surrounded by a modern housing estate, this windmill in a suburb of Leeds was converted to a house in the late 19th century. (Author's photo)

Leeds, Sugar Well Mill (WY)

Of the surviving windmills of Leeds, one can be found at the junction of Scott Hall Road and Potternewton Lane amid a housing estate and adjacent to a school. Built of locally quarried sandstone blocks, converted into a house, it went by the unusual name of *Sugar Well Hill Mill* or *Sugar Well Mill*, and was once the property of Jeremiah Dixon who 1775 advertised this *well-situated and good-accustomed windmill to let*, possibly not long after its completion. Up to the end of the nineteenth century two mills stood round about here, the one remaining converted to a dwelling in the 1880s, the other demolished in the 1930s.

Around 1898-99 the converted mill was lived in by Robert Bentley, who was over seventy years of age. He grew tomatoes for the wholesale trade. In 1921 the property was purchased by Samuel Ingham, who renovated the building that had been allowed to deteriorate to a bad state of repair, and carried on a business from the adjoining workshop. At that time he made measurements of the mill walls which he recorded as 3 feet 6 inches at the base and about 1 foot 9 inches at the top. There was also a very deep well-shaft in the yard about 5 feet 6 inches in diameter cut into the solid rock. This was later filled in.

Lelley (EY)

A windmill is first mentioned at Lelley in 1280. This was probably the mill replaced on the same site between 1770 and 1793. This windmill may or may not be the windmill that survives today. The deeds show that there was a mill here as far back as 1712, but it is not clear exactly when the present structure was built.

The deeds state a new mill was erected on the site in 1776, however, its height and a noticeable change in the

Adjacent to a farm, Lelley windmill stands derelict with much of its machinery still intact, while the boiler from the period when it was converted to steam power lies abandoned alongside the remains of the steam engine shed.

walling of the tower indicates that the windmill has seen alteration and enlargement. It is probable therefore, that only the lower half dates from the late-eighteenth century. Documents of 1790 and 1810 refer to the mill as *lately erected and built*. In subsequent deeds the word *lately* is omitted.

By 1873, steam power had been added to the mill, and the tall brick chimney of the engine house still remains on site, reminiscent of that at Cantley. The boiler too, survives, albeit in a dilapidated condition. Inside the windmill, much of the machinery survives as do part of the sails and with so much remaining there have been suggestions to preserve this windmill as a fine example of the county's industrial heritage.

Little Smeaton, the last remaining post-mill in Yorkshire, seen in 1934. It disappeared without trace in 1961 when it was said to be destined for a museum which never turned up!

Little Smeaton (WY)

It is not known when Little Smeaton windmill was erected, but its fame lies in the fact that it was possibly the last medieval wooden post-mill to survive in the county. Free-standing, the wood body of the mill was supported on a massive upright *post* that stood on a horizontal frame of two timbers crossed and jointed at right-angles. The upright post was further held in position by quarter bars of timber that ran between the horizontal cross-tree and the post. This arrangement allowed the entire body of the mill to be rotated into or out of the wind and so keep working in all types of wind conditions.

The remains of Lelley windmill today, with the tall chimney of the steam engine house alongside. (Author's photo)

While such an arrangement was considered the most common form and led to the name *post-mill*, it has been known for the wooden support frame to be made up of Y-shaped or H-shape timbers. It was also not unusual to find mills supported by only a central post buried deep into the earth, a somewhat short-sighted practice.

Normally the cross-tree was raised above the ground to allow air to circulate freely and keep the timber dry. However, a later practice was to bury the framework under an earth and stone mound to further support the often massive, mill structure above. This was often done when finances were tight and it was not possible to rebuild the frame structure. Much later, a type of post-mill evolved whereby the wooden mill body was erected on a raised stone or wood body which then formed a dry storage area beneath.

The life expectancy of most early post-mills was roughly between forty and fifty years. This fast dilapidation is partially explained by such hazards as rotting timbers, the gradual tilting of the structure under constant wind pressure, storm damage, and wood-boring insects.

Today, not one single example of a post-mill exists in the county, and it was a shame that the mill at Little Smeaton was not preserved. Although derelict for many years, it still retained the majority of its components.

Dennis Caton, an artist and historian, recalls the mills sudden and mysterious demise one August week in 1961.

Little Smeaton windmill [situated on the north bank of the river Went, six miles south-east of Pontefract], *then, was of very special interest. I went to the village one day in August of that year, and proceeded to make a careful drawing of what remained of it. Dusk set in before I could complete the work, so I was obliged to pack up my things and go home with the drawing not quite finished.*

A few days later, I went again to Little Smeaton with the intention of putting the finishing touches to the work, but when I got there — lo and behold — the mill had vanished ... almost without trace.

Mr Caton went on to state, the villagers were informed by those dismantling the windmill, that it was destined to be-erected in the grounds of a museum eventually. It never was and has disappeared completely.

Low Hawsker near Whitby (NY)

In 1557 two windmills in the Whitby district were conveyed to Richard Chlomley by John York, who had them off the Earl of Warwick in 1551. One of these may have been the windmill at Low Hawsker as this place is mentioned in the list of lands and manors. Notwithstanding, the windmill still standing here today is mentioned in the nineteenth century, being either built or rebuilt in brick sometime in the mid-1800s by a Mr Burnett and his nephew, John Burnett.

The production of ground corn at Low Hawsker came to a dramatic halt in August 1868. Following the events described in the *Whitby Gazette* below, it may be that the mill was restored and continued milling for some years after, although by 1935 when Karl Wood the noted Lincolnshire artist painted it, it was derelict.

Amid a complex of farm buildings, the windmill at Low Hawsker is used as a farm store. (Author's photo)

On Tuesday last, Hawsker Mill was completely destroyed by fire. The mill was a solid structure, built of brick only a few years ago and was carried on by Mr George Burnett, the owner, who resided in the adjoining house, which communicated with the mill. On Monday night, Mr Burnett was grinding corn in the mill until 10 o'clock. He fastened up the premises a little after ten, having with him when he did so a candle, the flame of which was exposed, and may have caused the conflagration. He then went to bed, but between one and two in the morning, he was awoke, and fancying that he saw a blaze, he got up and discovered that the mill was enveloped in flames. He immediately raised an alarm, and a young man was dispatched on horseback to Whitby for assistance. Mr George Buchannan, the agent for the Yorkshire Insurance Office, in which the property was insured, communicated with, and the result was that a fire engine, drawn by two horses, and accompanied by the fire brigade, proceeded to the scene of the conflagration. On their arrival, they found that the flames had made great progress, and caused much havoc; the interior of the mill, with all it contained, being entirely destroyed. The dwelling-house and sheds were in imminent danger, but by prompt and vigorous use of an adequate water supply, the fire was arrested, and the residence saved from injury, but the cart-shed, stable, and granary, which adjoined the mill, were burnt down. There was a great quantity of flour and wheat in the mill, which were destroyed, as were also the machinery and other effects therein. About six in the morning, the fire was nearly subdued, and the mill-wands fell and were broken to pieces. Two stacks of hay close to were saved, the fire being prevented from reaching them. The fire may be said to have burnt itself out, and ended in the complete destruction of the mill, and buildings and property mentioned. The damage is estimated at £1000. The owner's loss by the destruction of the mill and buildings is covered by insurance in the Yorkshire Office, but his stock-in-trade, we hear, is only partially insured. We understand the adjoining house was not insured. Mr Superintent Clarkson, Sergeant Martindale, and several constables were in attendance, and rendered effective aid. The origin of the fire has not yet be ascertained.

Mappleton near Hornsea (EY)

Today an empty shell, it retains its original cap though now dilapidated, mentioned by Gregory in *East Yorkshire Windmills* as a fine example of the Lincolnshire Cap, a type universally fitted on towers mills in the East Riding. This in cross-section is formed of a simple double ogee curve.

Mappleton Mill was erected in 1798 of brick, which was later cement rendered and tarred. Three storeys high, an internal staircase can be traced in the brickwork between the second and third floors. It measures internally 20 feet across and has two doors facing directly opposite each other, a not uncommon arrangement found in many mills. Cast to one side, a millstone remains. This measures 53 inches in diameter and is six inches thick. A large square nut in the centre measures seven inches by seven inches.

At what period it ceased to operate as a windmill is not known. Karl Wood painted it in June 1935 and shows it converted to a house. A photograph in Roy Gregory's book also shows it as a dwelling. At what date it stopped being a home is also not known, but certainly today every sign of it been used for human habitation is swept away — and if it was a house, was the millstone simply buried under the floor-boards at that period?

The remains of Mappleton windmill as they remain today. (Author's photo)

Market Weighton (EY)

There are no medieval references to corn windmills at Market Weighton, but there is an early reference to a wind bark mill there connected with the tanning industry. The first significant mention of corn mills occurs in the nineteenth century, when there was at least four corn windmills. In 1822 William Baines lists five corn millers, William Cade, Market Place; John and Robert Dawson, Hungate; James Peart, St Helen's Square, William Vause, Cave Road, George Scott, Market Place.

The only mill to survive into the twentieth century, was the one on Cave Road, a tower mill built of brick, erected in the typical manner of East Riding windmills. This was demolished around 1970.

The windmill at Market Weighton in 1935, showing the then recently blocked up door and windows.

Moor Monkton (NY)

A windmill is shown to the south of Moor Monkton on Jeffery's map of 1772, standing along the edge of Hessey Moor. This may be the same windmill and site that was mentioned with *a passage of and beyond the waters of the Ouse and Nidd* in 1526.

Photographed in 1942 it is seen very much truncated and ruinous. It was also painted by Karl Wood in 1933 who illustrated it without sails or cap and somewhat taller in height.

Moor Monkton windmill in a ruinous state in 1942.

Muston near Filey (NY)

On the outskirts of Filey, in a field bordering the A1039, stands the shell of a brick-built windmill. Known as *Muston Mill*, its served the adjoining parish of that name, and was possibly associated with nearby *Muston Grange*, which it overlooks.

A windmill was first recorded here in 1341, and mentioned frequently from then on in manorial records. The present mill is constructed of machined red brick and probably only dates from the nineteenth century, perhaps replacing an earlier wood post-mill that stood in 1826. A noticeable change in the brickwork suggests that this mill was either enlarged or partially rebuilt during its short life span, the mill being derelict by 1932.

Standing on a prominent rise, the windmill is short in stature due to its position and small in circumference, measuring only 25 feet in diameter. In 1822 Baines' *Directory* states the corn miller at Muston was William Collins.

Standing in a field on the outskirts of Filey, Muston windmill is possibly associated with nearby Muston Grange. (Author's photo)

Nafferton (EY)

In 1822 William Parker was described as corn miller, coal and lime merchant. As the windmill which remains today was only erected in 1829, it is possible that this replaced an earlier wooden post-mill, or there were two mills in Nafferton. Originally standing four storeys high, at one period a painting of a windmill graced the outside wall to advertise the trade of the miller. This was later replaced by the present advertising artwork at a time when the windmill ceased producing corn and ground animal feed.

Built alongside the Bridlington Road, steam power was added in 1840, and by 1892, it was described as the *old windmill*.

Nafferton windmill in 1992. It still stands empty ten years later. (Author's photo)

Newholm near Whitby (NY)

At Newholm, two miles west of Whitby just off the A171 Guisborough Road, only the mill house survives today of the windmill that once stood here just on the outskirts of the village. On some older maps, the mill was shown as *Burnt Mill*, but no explanation exists for this name. At what date the windmill ceased operations is unclear, but certainly by 1935 it was disused and under the ownership of Sir John Harrowing. He allowed its inspection at that date for the purposes of recording the mill with a view to proposing its preservation along with the other eight or nine reported to exist in the district at that time.

Newholm Mill on the outskirts of Whitby has been demolished, but the mill house survives. Drawing by Margaret L. Clark, circa 1930.

North Anston (WY)

A wooden post-mill was photographed at North Anston around 1930. This free-standing mill raised on the usual arrangement of a post, cross-tree and braced trestle, was powered by four shuttered sails. However, it is possible that two mills stood in the village during the same period, as another post-mill was photographed in ruins about the same date. This second mill stood in Bell's Field, off the Woodsett Road. In this instance the post and cross-tree were enclosed in a roofed roundhouse. Remains of the wands show that it was turned by four, common cloth sails. As a consequence, it must be assumed that two windmill stood on separate sites despite there being no documentary evidence.

On Jeffery's map of 1772 only one windmill is marked. This suggests that one of the two mills was erected after this date, as shuttered sails only came into common usage after being invented about this year.

The post-mill at North Anston around 1930. Photo: Rotherham Central Library, Archives & Local Studies Section.

Norton Mill as a shell in 1942.

Norton near Doncaster (SY)

pictures, and no less than 139 in Yorkshire, the majority of his works being produced during the 1930s, and the entire collection today, rests in the hands of the Lincolnshire Museums Service.

Today the mill still survives restored outwardly to a semblance of its original glory and is a Grade II listed monument. Standing six storeys in height, it is built of brick, rendered, and finished with an ogee-style cap based on descriptions provided by local residents. Its original date of foundation is unknown, but undoubtedly dates from the nineteenth century, possibly a rebuilding on an earlier site.

The rendering of a windmill with either tar or cement was necessary in numerous cases to provide a weather-proof exterior as the majority of windmills were, erected in open, exposed and elevated positions. As a consequence they took the full brunt of inclement weather conditions. Both stone, and especially brick, needed to be protected.

Beautiful — the windmill at Norton has been converted into a charming house. (Author's photo)

By 1932, the windmill at Norton, north of Doncaster off the Selby road, was derelict. At that date Karl Wood painted it. The achievements of this man, who was born in Nottingham in 1888 and later moved to Gainsborough, where he became an art master at the Grammar School there, provides us with details of many windmills in the early decades of the twentieth century. Karl Wood painted in total 1,394 windmill

Old Malton (NY)

In the yard of *Windmill Farm*, near Eden Camp War Museum at Old Malton, stand the remains of a three-storey red-brick windmill, which serves as a farm store. Its date of building is unknown, nor is it known when the mill ceased production. The sails, it is said, were blown off in a gale on 26 October 1906, but the tenant in 1990 told me he recalls sails being removed around 1952, *as the clattering [noise of them] frightened the yearling horses*. Karl Wood painted a mill at Malton in the 1930s — undoubtedly this mill — and at that period it was shown as redundant.

The windmill at Old Malton dominates the farmyard in which it stands. Today it is used for storage. (Author's photo)

Between 1851 and 1881 it was known as *Jolly Mill*, but the name may have been a corruption of *Folly Mill* and if so, suggests an earlier structure. The name *Folly Mill* may have originated under the same terms as *Folly Mill* at Bridlington, which is shown on Wood's map of 1828 as stood on Mill Lane, near *the Hollows*. Prior to 1828 the lane at Bridlington is recorded as Folly Mill Lane. As a mill was on this site in 1793, it would suggest at the commencement of this windmill, the locals thought the enterprise a risky one, being situated so far outside the town, possibly even folly!

Belonging to the Fitzwilliam estate, an old estate map undated, shows the present windmill at Old Malton and farm situated in a large open area called *Old Malton Moor* close to a large pond known as *Borough Mere* and still in existence. A track or mill-way is shown leading from the mill to the village of Old Malton.

The shell of the windmill at Osgodby surrounded by farm buildings in 1934.

Osgodby (EY)

At Osgodby a windmill was worked throughout the nineteenth century, and stood near Cliffe Road, south east of the village. As there is no mentioned of an earlier mill in manorial records, nor is a mill shown on Jeffery's map of 1772, then it is probable that the history of windmilling only began here at the commencement of the nine-teenth century.

According to Baines *Directory of Yorkshire*, in 1822, the corn miller was Michael Brown.

Patrington Haven (EY)

At Patrington, two mills were recorded from about 1340 – becoming later East and West Mills. *East Mill* was rebuilt in 1426-7 and *West Mill* was repaired in 1544-5. Originally a post-mill rising from a central pit dug into the ground, and not the more conventional type whereby the post was supported by a cross-tree framework, it was *through the strong wind and because of the age of the same mill that East Mill was from the roof thrown down and destroyed in the month of January within the time of this Account* [1426]. William Duffield was responsible for its rebuilding, the total expenditure for this amounting to £15 7s 1$^1/_2$d and the itemized account, submitted to the Archbishop of York for his inspection, survives to this day.

A study of the account shows that the entire windmill was constructed on site, even down to the manufacture of the nails. The account also indicates that when heavy labour was required, such as when raising the main post, the extra men recruited where unpaid, and worked solely for their food. From the amount of money expended on this item, a large number of labourers must have been engaged in its construction.

The windmills of Patrington were sold off by the Crown, their owner, in the seventeenth century. Both mills existed in the late-eighteenth century, however, and were probably the post-mill and smock-mill, on different sites, mentioned in 1802. *West Mill* beside the Winestead road, was later demolished, but a tower mill was erected on the road to the Haven in 1810 by G & W Boyd, millwrights. *East Mill*, on the Welwick Road, and *Patrington Haven Mill* were both using steam power as well as wind power by the 1870s. They remained in use until about 1940. A third corn-mill, worked by steam power, was built in Ings Lane in 1855, but was short-lived, and by 1871 it was being used as a warehouse and was demolished. Of the two mills, East and West, only *West Mill*, which became known as *Patrington Haven Mill*, remains today.

The windmill at Patrick Haven, Patrington, dominates the skyline and is seen towering above the farm buildings. (Author's photo)

An unidentified windmill in Pontefract in 1934, then a derelict shell.

Pontefract (WY)

Being an ancient town with a castle, undoubtedly Pontefract had windmills at an early date, but no record survives of these. However, in the nineteenth century, three windmills existed, two of which were familiar landmarks for many years — *St Thomas Mill* and *Dandy Mill*. This later windmill, was erected about 1803, by a Dutchman who also erected Darrington windmill. *Dandy Mill* stood south of the railway line near to *Pontefract Castle* and the old church of All Saints. Tall and slim, it was built of brick and later tarred to keep it weather-tight. Somewhat unique in design, the base splayed outwards considerably from about ten feet above ground level. At some date in the early nineteenth century, a gas engine was installed to power the mill.

St Thomas Mill stood about half a mile from *Dandy Mill*, which was built by a Dutchman who was also responsible for the construction of Darrington windmill. In contrast to *Dandy Mill*, *St Thomas Mill* was small and squat in size, possibly because like so many other windmills, it was erected on a prominent eminence. Later, this windmill was converted to a dwelling.

Danby Mill, Pontefract, in 1934 when its sails had been removed.

St. Thomas Mill, Pontefract, in the 1930s after conversion to a house.

Ravenscar (NY)

At Ravenscar, situated on the coast between Whitby and Scarborough, stands a windmill bearing the date 1858 carved into the stone plinth. Built of worked stone blocks, it stands four storeys high.

Known as *Peak Mill*, when newly erected in the mid-nineteenth century, it was associated with an adjacent inn both leased by the owner to the miller, and an advertisement appeared in the *Whitby Gazette* to attract a suitable applicant:

MILLER WANTED

For a new windmill at Peak, near Stainton Dale at Scarborough. He must be a steady, industrious man with a good character, and one who thoroughly understands his business. If with a wife that could take charge of a small Inn, built near the Mill, it would be preferred.

Apply by letter, with terms, to Mr Hammond, Raven Hall, near Scarborough.

The derelict windmill at Ravenscar stands high on the moor above the North Sea. (Author's photo)

Riccall (NY)

The only surviving windmill of three that stood at Riccall, seen in 1935. It is now a restaurant.

In 1295 a windmill stood at Riccall. During the fifteenth century a second windmill was mentioned as belonging to the Bishop of Durham. By 1803 this mill had disappeared, and its site was marked in documents by the description *the old Mill Hill* in *West Field*. During the 1840s, however, there were two windmills at Riccall, one standing in *West Field* and another in *East Field*. *West Field Mill* had steam power by 1889, but later reverted back to wind power and survived until about 1910. *East Field Mill* by contrast, was not mentioned again, and was later replaced by a steam corn-mill.

North of the village, in the hamlet of Preston in Riccall township, a windmill stood in the thirteenth century. A second windmill was erected around 1420, built in the open fields. This was possibly a post-mill replaced in 1813. Another windmill was mentioned as being newly built around 1825, but by the middle years of the nineteenth century it had been demolished. The surviving mill here was eventually converted to steam power, but ceased to operate soon after.

It was while engaged in work on the mill at Riccall during the latter years of the nineteenth century, that George Reed, millwright, of Howden, was fatally injured when he fell from the top of the windmill tower.

The surviving windmill at Riccall is said to date back to 1290. The original mill was replaced in 1811. This brick tower windmill had four sails and three pairs of grindstones. The walls are 18 inches thick. It was converted to steam power, but fell into disrepair in 1911, when it was refurbished as a private residence. This was later sold and today the mill survives as a restaurant.

Rotherham, Dalton Brook (WY)

Another windmill that survived into the nineteenth century at Rotherham, was that known as *Dalton Brook Mill*. This windmill was photographed around the end of that century, and while it is shown as derelict and with no sails, it is interesting to note that it was not recorded on the 1st edition Ordnance Survey Map of 1890. The mill house, however, still stood and later became an inn. Today it continues to survive and has recently been converted into housing.

The photograph shows a tall narrow tower mill, heightened at some previous date, as there is a marked difference in the brickwork. Covered by a Dutch-style ogee-shaped cap, this shows evidence of having supported a fantail. Adjacent is the tall chimney of what was undoubtedly a steam engine house, and at some date it was obviously powered by this force. Interestingly, I can find no millers listed in any nineteenth century trade directories for this windmill. Possibly already by this period it was no longer in operation, superceded by the two mills at Doncaster Gate.

The windmill shell at Dalton Brook, Rotherham in the 1930s. The chimney for the steam engine stands alongside. Photo: Rotherham Central Library, Archives & Local Studies Section.

Rotherham, Doncaster Gate (WY

In the town of Rotherham, two windmills still stood in 1827 at Doncaster Gate with boundaries along St Anne's Hill, and were shown complete at that date in Christopher Thompson's *Hallamshire Scrapbook*. These were tower mills but no doubt replaced earlier post-mills. A photograph taken about fifty years later shows them derelict, one completely roofless and devoid of sails, while the second still retained partial sails. This indicates that the earlier drawing is perhaps not as accurate as one might suppose.

Built of stone, the two mills at Doncaster Gate each stood five storeys high and were practically cylindrical, with hardly any banter to their walls. One had a curious circular room running around the base of the tower, no doubt erected as some form of storage area. On a nineteenth century map dated 1890, one of these two mills, presumably the more ruined, is described as the *old windmill*.

In 1822 the two millers listed in Baines *Directory of Yorkshire* are Matthew Crossby and Richard Tasker, who operated independently even though the windmills were situated very near to each other.

Two Rotherham mills at Doncaster Gate in the 1930s. Photo: Rotherham Central Library, Archives & Local Studies Section.

Scarborough (NY)

In nineteenth century Scarborough, it was said that *the sails of four windmills stood out against the sky* — Greengates Mill at the foot of Mill Street, North Marine Road (Greengate Lane is the old name for North Marine Road); *Albion Mill* on the North Cliffe, which was demolished shortly after 1860 for the erection of *Osborne House*, which became part of *Gibson's Hotel* — this was a tower mill with four sails shown on Wood's map of 1828 and seen on an engraving of the Seaman's Hospital; the *Common Mill*, on Mill Street, Victoria Road (often called *Harrison's Mill*); and one on the South Cliffe where St Martin's church stood.

This latter windmill on the South Cliffe was first recorded in 1523 and mentioned again in 1556. Earlier, in 1320 *a windmill belonging to the Crown* may have been this mill. Interestingly, in 1660-61, it is recorded that *the inhabitants [of Scarborough] knew of only one windmill, pulled down in the Civil War* — a statement possibly suggestive that more than one windmill stood in the early-seventeenth century.

John Wood's map of 1828 also shows another windmill occupying a site on North Cliffe, off the Whitby road, not far from *Albion Mill* which may be this mill, but also may have been a separate windmill making a total of five existing in that century.

In Sotheran's *Scarborough Guide* dated 1787, a new windmill is suggested to have been erected about this date, mentioned in a short passage that reads:

Bread, at Scarborough, has been humorously pronounced the wholesomest in England, as being lighter … than that of most corporate towns; by some ounces in the sixpenny loaf! But it must also be observed, that wheat is, upon an average, dearer here than at the neighbouring markets; and so, in proportion of about a seventh until the late building and establishment, of that ample windmill, which now supplies, and decorates the town.

To which windmill the writer is referring is not known, but it may have been *Common Mill*, off Victoria Road often referred to later as *Harrison's Mill*, which is thought to have been put up around this period.

In 1819 there was an auction of a windmill at the *Star Inn*. This stood on the edge of town near the end of the present

Queen Street that runs between Castle Road and Newborough, which was then the main carriage road to Whitby.

The windmill to be sold, a brick tower mill with four patent sails, was in the possession of a Mr English and Mr Wilson, and contained two pairs of French stones, one pair four feet six inches across and the other four feet four inches in diameter. Beside the mill was *a commodious granary, a cart shed, three stables and a yard.*

Two 19th century engravings of Scarborough. Top is the new workhouse with Harrison's Mill behind. Below is the Seaman's Hospital with Albion Mill on the left.

Harrison's Mill, Scarborough, in the late 19th century with members of Harrison's family standing outside the mill entrance.

Scarborough, Harrison's Mill (NY)

Just off Victoria Road, up Mill Street, not far from the railway station, stands a restored brick windmill. Dating from the late-eighteenth century, a succession of mills have stood on this site. It was last worked as a mill by Albert Price Harrison, who had it off his father Moses Harrison, who lived nearby at *Calthorpe House*, Victoria Road (at the bottom of Mill Street) which today is known as *Villa Marina*.

Originally called Common Mill, it was erected on land belonging to Scarborough Corporation and was operated privately on leasehold. Indeed, Corporation records contain such leases dating back to 1601. Until the end of the nineteenth century the windmill stood in open countryside on common land, hence its name. Gradually as the size of Scarborough increased, the mill became surrounded by urban development.

In the Civil War period, in 1645, the windmill was used by the Parliamentary commander, General Sir John Meldrum, as an artileery observation post during the Siege of Scarborough.

Moses Harrison ran the mill in partnership with his brother Francis as a corn and seed merchant business. It is thought Moses bought the windmill about 1850 from a Mr Harland, who later became connected with the Belfast shipbuilders, Harland and Wolff. After coming into the possession of his son, Albert, it continued in use until the autumn of 1927.

First powered by six sails, some or all were blown down in a gale in 1880, falling on a cowshed and killing a cow. Only four sails were used afterwards. These were removed in 1898. From this time, the mill was fitted up with a rare twelve horse-power gas-turbine engine.

When Moses and Francis Harrison first ran the windmill it became known as *Harrison's Mill* and remained so. It is supposed that the windmill was erected around 1785 by Thomas Robinson. In 1796 it was owned by a Dr Belcombe, who had it off a Jack Binns.

A former employee at the mill, Mr Charles Ditchburn, who started work at the mill aged fourteen and then earned fifteen shillings per week, said that *a huge wooden shaft ran up the centre of the windmill from a five ton cherry-wood wheel. Wooden cogs drove the iron wheels which, in turn, powered the stone grinding machinery and that once a week the whole assembly had to be lifted up on two huge bottle-jacks so that the phosphor-bronze cup in which the central shaft rested, could be oiled.*

When the grinding of corn ceased, the structure gradually fell into disrepair and was used for a variety of purposes including seed storage and newspaper distribution. In 1985 permission to demolish the mill and build flats was sought. Ironically, this scheme was rejected as it was thought the flats would overshadow nearby housing.

In 1988, Stephen Beecroft and his partner, Irene Mapplebeck, purchased the mill, renovating it and turning it into an award-winning hotel. Tragically Stephen died of a heart attack shortly afterwards and the mill changed hands. Julie and Simon Boddy became the owners and further developed the site. In July 1997, Angela and Roland Thompson bought the mill and introduced the Tea Rooms and Toy Museum. The latter is based on Roland's collection and is displayed in the windmill. It comprises around 3,000 items, mainly post-1960.

Harrison's Mill today, converted to a guest house, cafe and toy museum, with its sails restored but unable to turn. (Photo R. Thompson)

Seaton Ross, Preston's & Fisher's Mills (EY)

Little is known about the early years of windmilling at Seaton Ross. That two mills stood for many years is undeniable, one called *Preston's Mill*, the other *Fisher's Mill*. This was fitted with four patent sails. *Preston's Mill* was one of the last two windmills in the East Riding to operate by wind power and was dismantled in 1951 when its five sails were taken down. A photo of Preston's Mill appears on the front cover, showing evidence of milling in 1935.

In 1839, the *Hull Advertiser* dated 11 January carried a story about the partial destruction of a mill at Seaton Ross which may have been Preston's Mill… *The beautiful corn mill (which is upwards of seven storeys high) belonging to Mr R Cook, of Seaton Ross, had the top completely carried off, together with part of the wall, which, before it fell, presented a grand but awful appearance; from the top to about the fifth storey the wall on each side opened and shut twelve or fourteen inches, as the sails were going round the gearing. The stones were laid on their faces to prevent its progress, but which in reality aggravated its previous effects. The neighbour's and tenant were in the act of carrying water to the top to prevent the mill firing, when it came down altogether into an adjoining garden, the top etc being completely smashed to pieces.*

In 1822 Baines' *Directory* gave the names of the two millers as Matthew Cook and Robert Rook, the latter an obvious error for Cook!

Fisher's Mill, Seaton Ross, in June 1935.

Selby (WY)

Despite its size and prominence, and the fact that a great deal of corn was shipped from here via the River Ouse, Selby supported few corn windmills. The majority of mills here from ancient times were water- or steam-powered and ground flax. Selby Abbey had a windmill in the town known as *Abbey Soke Mill*. This remained until the nineteenth century and was a tall, brick-built structure that was toward the end of its life powered by steam. A plan of Selby dated 1800 shows it was the only windmill in existence standing on Mill Lane alongside Mill Beck. When *Abbey Soke Mill* had four sails, the cap was the unusual ridged boat-style suggesting it possibly dated from the early-eighteenth century or before. By 1933 it was derelict and much reduced in size.

During the Middle Ages, John de Markenfield, clerk, *gave one messuage, one windmill, four tofts, and three oxgangs of land to fund one chaplain to celebrate divine offices every day … in the church of Brayton*. This was no doubt the wood post-mill at Brayton that survived well into modern times.

Within Selby parish, the manor of Burn was recorded has having two windmills in 1560, but only one was mentioned with lands between 1579 and

The remains of Selby windmill in 1934.

Sewerby near Bridlington (EY)

At Sewerby, on the outskirts of Bridlington, a windmill is first mentioned in the early-fourteenth century and frequently thereafter. In 1619 a windmill stood in the fields of Sewerby *nigh unto Bempton*, probably on a site close to the boundary with Bempton which was occupied in the eighteenth century and later, by a mill known as either Speeton or Bempton Mill.

A miller was last recorded at Sewerby in 1937, and the windmill was derelict by 1969. A noted feature of *Sewerby Mill*, was that the cross to which the sails were fixed, displayed a most interesting variant on the East Riding type which had its own distinct shape. At Sewerby the variation was that the lip was replaced by a pair of lugs. Today, the remains of Sewerby windmill are incorporated into the office of a Caravan Park that occupies the site.

Constructed of brick, and seemingly never rendered, an obvious waist and change in brickwork illustrates that the windmill was heightened at some point in time before becoming redundant.

The remains of Sewerby windmill have today been incorporated into a holiday chalet on a caravan site. (Author's photo)

Shelf near Bradford (WY)

In the Bradford district the last corn windmill to survive was that at Shelf, on the Halifax Road. This dilapidated and crumbling structure remained until the early-1960s when it was pulled down. It was built of locally quarried stone and erected during the nineteenth century. To the end it retained most of its original machinery and was photographed in 1942 minus only its cap and sails and Karl Wood painted it in 1937, also showing it derelict without cap or sails.

The most famous mill in the Bradford area was that at Wibsey, situated in the High Street. This replaced an earlier mill recorded in 1653 on a different site to the east of Wibsey village. The second *Wibsey Mill* was erected in 1681 by William Pollard, a Brierley landowner. The contract for its construction was awarded to John Marsden on 5 November, who built the main structure. The sails, mill-post and other internal timber fittings was undertaken by John Robinson. When complete, an old drawing shows the mill had a conical cap and was almost cyclindrical in shape, with little taper or *batter* to its walls and few window openings.

In 1802 the mill structure was damaged in a whirlwind. A report in the *Leeds Intelligencer* dated 8 February described how the top of the windmill, occupied by J Briggs was completely blown away. One of the sails was broken off and carried a distance of 80 yards or more, destroying a house chimney in the process. The cost of repairing the damage to the mill was estimated at £150. This mill was rebuilt in 1861. Accounts show that the masons worked for 138 days in hewing materials at

Hill Stone Quarry, for which wages amounting to £7 2s 6d were paid. Beer and other victuals were provided at an additional cost of 27 shilling.

Wibsey windmill was demolished in 1838 and the stone and timber was used to construct some cottages along an ancient trackway named Windmill Lane. These cottages and the *Windmill Inn*, which remain today, mark the site of *Wibsey Mill*.

In Bowling township stood *Dickinson's Mill* on a triangular patch of land at the junction of three old lanes. The windmill disappeared but the triangular patch of land survived long after, and on it stood five quaint cottages known as *T'miln-haases*.

Grenwood's Corn Mill was the first in Bradford to be steam-operated and was erected at Wibsey Bankfoot in 1837.

On Jeffery's map of 1772 windmills are shown between Bolton and Eccleshill on the outskirts of Bradford, and the mill at Wibsey is marked.

In 1822 the corn miller was Robert Woodhead.

The derelict mill at Shelf, near Bradford, in 1942.

Sherburn-in-Elmet (WY)

The windmill remains at Sherburn-in-Elmet on the outskirts of Leeds were last mentioned in 1959. At this date they were described as a site only, suggesting that the ruins photographed in 1934 had long since disappeared. The stump walls, little more than eight feet tall, show that it was constructed of brick. A feature of interest that is shown, is an arrangement similar to the mill at Bramham, where a semi-circular arch below the windmill possibly was designed to provide dry storage.

In 1822 the corn miller was Joseph Anderson.

The last remains of Sherburn Mill in 1934, with an arched storage area below the mill, not unlike that at Bramham Mill.

Skelton-on-Ure (NY)

Little is known concerning the windmill at Skelton-on-Ure. It was named *Kirby Mill* and probably dates from the nineteenth century. No windmill here is marked on Jeffery's map of 1772, usually considered accurate. In 1822 the corn miller was Charles Williamson. Never converted to steam or electric *Kirby Mill* was a tall seven storey brick mill powered by four sails.

Karl Wood painted the mill in April 1933 at which time it was derelict, still standing in 1942 in the same condition. Since that date it has completely disappeared.

Kirby Mill, Skelton-on-Ure, in 1942.

Skidby (EY)

Standing on a low ridge of the Wolds, the black tower and white sails of Skidby windmill are easily spotted when travelling along the road toward the Humber Bridge from Beveley.

Built in 1821 by the Garton family of Beverley, it replaced an earlier mill that had stood here since the Middle Ages. This earlier mill in 1388 was leased from the lord of the manor for £1 6s 8d per annum. The lease contained provision for its repair and upkeep whereby the lord was to provide the main timbers and millstones, while the tenant was responsible for the remainder of the fabric and fittings. In 1854 the windmill was bought by Joseph Thompson, and it remained with his family until taken over by the Weston Group. At the time Thompson bought it, the mill was considered the best in the district. In the twentieth century the mill was powered by electricity set up in 1954, but retained its sails.

Seventy-two feet tall to the curb, the Lincolnshire cap measures another seventeen feet. Each of the four sails is nine feet wide and has a sweep of 28 feet. Each sail arm consists of a wooden frame with canvas vanes. Damaged by lightning in 1946, it was the last windmill to work in the county, and as such brought a response by the Society for the Protection of Ancient Buildings for its preservation. In 1968 the Weston Group donated the mill complex with machinery to Beverley Rural District Council. The Council established a small museum of relics connected with grinding corn, while preserving it as a working mill.

The windmill boasts three pairs of stones — one French pair for flour, and two pairs of Peak stones for grinding feed. It is the only surviving wind-powered mill in Yorkshire and operates as a working museum open to visitors. (Winter - weekends; Summer - Wednesday to Sunday; tel. 01482 848405) It is now owned by the East Riding of Yorkshire Council.

The interior of Skidby Mill showing the three pairs of stones used for grinding both corn and animal feed.

Skidby windmill looked much the same in 1935 as it does today. It is Yorkshire's only working windmill, and is open to view at certain times. (Author's photo)

South Duffield (EY)

Drax Priory had a windmill at South Duffield that was mentioned in 1311. A windmill was shown on Jeffery's map of 1772. A windmill was worked in the village throughout the nineteenth century. In 1935 when photographed, it can be seen to be complete except for the sails, which by this date had become broken and a pair lost, rendering the mill inoperable. It was probably about this time that the mill permanently ceased working, as it is possible that for some time just prior to this date from the evidence of the photograph, the windmill was operated with only two sails.

The mill at South Duffield in 1935, shortly after closure and showing the broken and missing sails.

The post-mill at South Skirlaugh in 1934.

South Skirlaugh (EY)

One of the last post-mills to survive in Yorkshire stood at South Skirlaugh. It was said that the mill had been there since 1250. This clearly cannot be, but there is evidence to suggest a fairly early date for its construction. The evidence is to be found in the shape of the cap roof, uncommon in this county, but very similar to *Bourn Mill* in Cambridgeshire, known to exist in 1637. Rex Wailes, the noted windmill authority attaches some importance to roof shape as a dating feature, explaining that as mills attained more power a larger brake wheel was built onto the wind-shaft. To allow space for these larger brake wheels the pitched roof tended to become more rounded, like the Gothic arch of a church, suggesting that here at South Skirlaugh the mill probably dated from the seventeenth century.

In 1822 the miller was Robert Waldby. Of interest also, is the fact that unlike most wooden post-mills that contained two pairs of millstones, one in the breast and one in the tail, Skirlaugh contained three pairs of stones in 1852.

Karl Wood painted the windmill at Skirlaugh in October 1933 and shows it only partially sailed and clearly not working. It was demolished in 1944.

Sproatley (EY)

The windmill at Sproatley outside of which appear John Rank and his family. He was the founder of the famous Rank milling dynasty. (Photo from author's collection)

In 1825, John Rank (1801-63), aged twenty-four, rented the tenancy of *Sproatley Mill* built five years earlier. Until then, the Rank family had been farmers in the East Riding since the mid-sixteenth century. John Rank's move into milling was to be the first step in making the name of Rank synonymous with that occupation through five generations.

Three years later, in 1828, John Rank bought the copyhold of Sproatley windmill for £655 *and in accordance did fealty upon his admittance to the manor as a vassal*. The purchase of consisted of two roods of land on which stood a wind corn mill, dwelling house and hereditaments *now in the occupation of the said John Rank*.

In 1841, John and his wife and family moved to Hull to take on a mill there. However, his eldest daughter married Slater Eyre, a miller, and the young couple took over the mill at Sproatley and remained there for many years as manager. In 1854 John Rank sold *Sproatley Mill* to Sir Clifford Constable, the lord of the manor of Sproatley.

At what date the windmill ceased operation or disappeared is not known. Karl Wood did not paint it, and this suggests it had gone by the first decade of the 1930s.

Stutton near Tadcaster (NY)

At Stutton, familiar to motorists travelling along the A64 York to Leeds road, near to Tadcaster, a windmill stands on a pronounced conical prominence overlooking the highway. Built of magnesian limestone quarried nearby, where the quarry pit can still be seen on the opposite side of the road, the tower although four storeys high, appears short and squat, and the walls have a distinctive taper. These are so constructed as to give added strength to the stonework in its elevated position. Internally, the mill measures approximately twenty-two feet in diameter and has walls two feet thick. On the ground floor is a fireplace, with the flue built within the walling.

Possibly erected in the eighteenth century, inside the derelict shell are the remains of two millstones. Both the upper and lower millstones are marked with a cross. As the mill originally belonged to a noted Catholic family, it is possibly that the devout owners had the stones blessed by a priest. Another interesting feature of the mill at Stutton is that in shape, size and material, it is an identical twin to the demolished windmill at Laughton-en-le-Morthen, near Rotherham, which was known as *Carr Mill*.

The shell of Stutton windmill in 1961. It survives today in a similar condition. (Author's photo)

Thorne (SY)

In Thorne stood six windmills, all shown on the 1853 Ordnance Survey map. The earliest documented reference to a windmill here occurs in the courts rolls of 1275, when William Scutard was accused in his absence of falsely setting the stones *in order to steal the flour of the customary tenants*.

Another windmill is mentioned in a royal grant from King Charles I to Cornelius Vermuyden dated 1627, which notes a mill worth fifteen shillings a year in rent, once owned by Edward Ferrers and Francis Phipps, esquire. However, on Jeffery's map of 1772, only four windmills are shown but undoubtedly one of these is the windmill referred to.

The town of Thorne developed along a low ridge of sand lying roughly north and south. The ridge, known as *High Trod*, is only about two miles in length, yet its height, only nine metres above sea level, in an otherwise flat landscape, was sufficient to encourage the building of windmills. In 1629 a mill was erected at the top of Brooke Street, or Crust's Mill Road as it was known in the nineteenth century. This mill was called Bellwood's Mill. It was a wooden post-mill, the stones turned by four cloth sails. At a later date, the open space beneath the windmill between the cross-tree which held it up, was enclosed to provide storage space. Unfortunately the sails of this mill blew down at an unknown date in the nineteenth century and it fell into disuse, causing it to be pulled down on the eve of World War I.

Only one windmill remains today, a brick tower mill on North Eastern Road. It is remembered as *Oates' Mill*, after the last family to work it. Before that however, its was known firstly as *Priestley's Mill* then *Gravil's Mill*. The shell stands five storeys high, and it had an ogee Dutch cap surmounted by a tall ball finial. The exterior was tar rendered, giving it a distinctive black appearance. The sails broke off about 1880, after which time the windmill was powered by a steam engine.

Past *Oates' Mill* and just before the crossroads, stood *Casson's Mill*. Over the crossroads to the right stood *Hemingway's Mill*. The fifth mill was *Oldfield's Mill* which stood in Southfield Road, not far from the top of Oldfield Road. The final windmill was called *Far Post Mill* and stood just to the south of Thorne North Railway Station and its name suggest that this was an wood old post mill. By 1907, however, only two windmills were shown as existing.

The windmills, as most mills, often took their names from the miller working them, and in common practice, often changed their names as the family died out or left the mill and it changed ownership. In 1822 William Baines *Directory* listed the following corn millers and flour dealers in the village Abraham Bradbury; Curtis Casson; Timothy Harrison; James Moore; John Oldfield; and Samuel Sails. Rather aptly, one of the few named village inns of Thorne in Baines *Directory* was the *Wind Mill*, run by George Hoyland, victualler.

The only one of a number of windmills in Thorne to survive is seen here in 1935 after conversion to a house.

Thornton-le-Clay (NY)

Little is known about the small redundant brick windmill that still survives today west of Thornton village. It was probably erected at the beginning of the nineteenth century. Standing on a slight eminence beyond the mill house, the shell measures internally approximately twenty feet in diameter, with walls that are 14 inches thick. Three storeys high, it appears to have been derelict for many years, and the present occupier of the mill house thinks that the previous owner sold off all the fixtures and fittings over forty years ago. Around 1913, however, it was known to have had both sails and a cap though not working. The owner at that date was considering turning the mill into a dwellinghouse.

Externally, the walls show signs of having been tarred to protect it from the elements as it stood in its isolated position overlooking the Vale of York. Interestingly, as in many villages, on the boundary the village name is mounted on two mill grindstones, one at each end of Thornton-le-Clay. Unusually small in diameter, possibly these were from the windmill here. At one time I was told, three millstones stood, one at each entrance to the village.

The ruined shell of Thornton-le-Clay mill stands on the outskirts of the village. (Author's photo)

Tollerton (NY)

The windmill at Tollerton possibly dates from the eighteenth century, but is not marked on Jeffery's map of 1772. In 1822 the corn millers were two brothers, George and John Suggitt, consequently if the mill was not standing at the time of Jeffery, then its date of erection could have been in the last quarter of that century, or at the very beginning of the nineteenth century. Little else is recorded of its history. It went out of use before the Second World War, and although efforts were made to preserve it, these failed.

It is said that while it stood empty a sail blew off in a gale. If this occurred, then it was repaired, as in August 1942 when the mill was being dismantled and this remarkable series of photographs was taken, it still had four sails. At this date the wands were removed and the machinery inside was taken away. The windmill stood as a derelict tower in 1959, and is today converted into a house though reduced in height.

Tollerton windmill in 1942 during dismantling.

The left hand photo was taken during dismantling in 1942 and shows details of the sails, such as the spider gear and shutters which opened and closed to regulate the speed of rotation.

The right hand photo was probably taken in 1961 after the mill had been standing derelict for almost twenty years.

Ulleskelf (NY)

Today a house, the windmill at Ulleskelf, not far from Tadcaster on the B1223 road heading toward Selby, is only small in height. The date of its erection is said to be 1770, and no medieval manorial records appear to mention any previous mills. Constructed of brick, an interesting corbel-table of the same material just below the top may be original and designed to support the revolving cap and is similar to the one at *Colton Mill*. It was converted into a house in 1932.

Adjacent, and now a separate property, the mill house has built into its boundary wall a millstone which no doubt came from the mill. This is unusually large, and measures five feet in diameter, which suggests for its size, in relation to the mill, the windmill possibly employed only one set of stones for grinding.

Ulleskelf windmill is small in size and was converted to a house in 1932. (Author's photo)

The 'boat' cap and sails of Ugthorpe mill in 1946 which replaced an earlier arrangement of different design. Unidentified photo from the author's collection.

Ugthorpe (NY)

The present windmill at Ugthorpe, standing as a prominent landmark in the moorland landscape and visible from the A171 which runs between Whitby and Guisborough, was erected in 1796 on the site of an earlier structure, possibly a post-mill. This windmill was a brick tower mill and had a domed cap that carried an automatic fan-tail for turning the top into the wind. The cap shown is a later replacement and from about 1946. Notice by this date that there is no fantail; undoubtedly the sails were turned into the wind by means of an internal gear system.

In 1860, Ugthorpe windmill was offered for sale and an advertisement to that effect appeared in the *Whitby Gazette*.

MR JOHN P LINTON WILL OFFER BY AUCTION, on Friday, the 10th August 1860, at Three o'clock in the Afternoon, at the house of Mr David Smallwood, the Black Bull Inn, in Ugthorpe, in the parish of Lythe, in the County of York, subject to such conditions as will be then and there produced, all the capital Freehold Corn WIND MILL, Dwellinghouse, and garden, with the small garth near the same, called 'Hunt House Garth' containing about One Acre situated at Ugthorpe aforesaid, now occupied by Messrs John and Robert Wilson, the owners.

The Mill contains Two Pairs of Stones — one French and the other Grey — a Cylinder, and all other conveniences for carrying on to the greatest advantage the Business of a prosperous Agricultural to the rising population of the district.

Standing isolated in a field, the remains of Ugthorpe windmill have been converted into a holiday home and are easily visible from the Whitby-Guisborough road. (Author's photo)

The high elevation of the mill gives it an advantage over the mills in the neighbourhood, and it is the only one in the extensive parish of Lythe.

Connected to this Property is a Right of Stray and Turbary on the extensive Common of Ugthorpe.

The property is Tithe-free, but subject to the payment of ten shillings per annum for Land Tax.

Further particulars may be had of the Owners; of the Auctioneers; or at the Offices of Messrs GRAY & PANNETT & ROBERT BRECKON, Solicitors, Whitby.

It is possible that at this point the mill was taken over by a Mr C Walker, as a bill-head for 1872 displays his name as *Miller & Corn Manufacturer*. Ugthorpe windmill was again under new management in 1889, when Robert Dobson purchased the mill and adjoining cottage for £105. He worked the windmill until his death in 1906 whereupon his son, Robert inherited the mill, worth then £150. By 1934, Robert Dobson, Jnr, had in turn rented the building to a miller named Wilkinson for an annual rent of £15. At the death of Robert Dobson, Jnr, the windmill was taken over by Eric Stonehouse, of Wakefield.

Ugthorpe windmill still stands on an eminence at the edge of the village and provides holiday accommodation for visitors to the area.

Walkington Mill in 1935.

Walkington (EY)

In 1850 a new brick tower mill replaced an earlier post-mill leased by John Todd which he possibly erected in 1721. Walkington Mill was particularly tall, and stood eight storeys high. Midway an external gallery ran around the tower and gave access to the sails, the evidence clearly visible. One feature of interest of this mill, was the kiln for drying the grain prior to milling. The chimney alongside was most probably for the drying shed, or possibly Walkington Mill was steam-powered by the date of this photograph in 1935.

In 1822 the corn miller was Timothy Loft. Karl Wood painted Walkington Mill in 1933 showing it derelict by this date.

Wentworth (WY)

The earliest reference to a windmill at Wentworth occurs in 1590, when a series of manorial by-laws was drawn up, one of which stated *every person within the lordship do grind his corn at the lord's windmill … *Failure to comply meant a fine of 3s 4d. As windmills have existed here for a long period and been built and rebuilt throughout the centuries, it is not clear to which windmill these by-laws refer. But a windmill obviously continued on one site at Wentworth, and was repaired between 1769 and 1770, when the Estate Account Books mention on 13 November 1769, *Christopher Evers in full for the repair of a windmill, etc upon quitting the same, £26 5s 0d*. A year later an entry dated 14 October 1770 reads, *John Marshall then and before for work done and materials found in and about repairing Wentworth windmill in full, £63 0s 6d*.

In 1745, Lord Malton, soon to become the 1st Marquis of Rockingham, *built a new wind miln* at Wentworth. This was probably the mill now known as **The Roundhouse**, in Clayfields Lane. Estate accounts record the *buying of eighty yards of sail cloth for the windmill*. Another entry shows a payment of £2 12s 6d to Jonathan Smith, millwright, while a further entry for the year ending 7 July 1745, mentions a payment for 158,000 bricks, undoubtedly for the windmill in the village, which is constructed of thin, handmade bricks on a stone base.

That two separate windmills stood hereabouts during the same period is almost certainly the case. Mention of repairs to a windmill in 1769 presupposes this, as it would hardly seem credible that a substantially built *new wind miln* barely twenty-four years old would be in need of attention by this date.

Unfortunately, however, the issue of the number of windmills at Wentworth during the eighteenth century is complicated and not made entirely clear when maps for the area are searched. No mills at Wentworth are shown on Joseph Dickenson's *Map of South Yorkshire* (1750), but a single windmill appears on Jeffery's map of 1772. Only one mill is marked on William Fairbank's 1778 *Plan of Wentworth*.

The list of alterations in the Wentworth Estate Rental of 1793 provides evidence though, which tends to support the idea that two windmills existed. A note recalls: *John Pearson*

The windmill at Wentworth has been converted into a dwelling called **The Roundhouse**. Photo: Rotherham Central Library, Archives & Local Studies Section.

abated out of his rents in consideration of the windmill not having been wrought part of this year, the same being taken down and rebuilt at Barrow. Obviously as one was removed another must have stood, as in the same year, Household Accounts show an entry of payment to *Anthony Boulby, bricklayer, for 14 days wages converting old windmill into a cottage called Saxon Tower — £1 15s 0d*. This was the *Roundhouse*, and the name **Saxon Tower** suggests that the ornamental crenellations that encircle the roof were his handiwork in 1793. Joseph Wormack became the first tenant at Martinmas of that year, paying a rent of £1 10s 0d annually. A year later, the wheels, etc from an *old mill* were sold by Leonard Wilkinson, an estate foreman.

With the mill went a *small house* for the use of the miller, but from what period this was provided is unknown. It was taken down in 1788, but in 1769 Christopher Evers rented the mill, house and garden for £18. In 1778 the mill was *not let*, but from thereon it was in operation until its eventual demise and conversion. The list of millers include Joseph Welsh, buried in Wentworth churchyard in 1781; Thomas Booth previous to 1784 in which year Benjamin Jackson replaced him and finally John Pearson who took possession in the latter half of 1791, and whose father possibly worked **Aldham Mill** at Wombwell.

Wetwang (EY)

The windmill at Wetwang, situated in the north-west corner of the village along Northfield Road, remained a post-mill throughout the eighteenth century. This was a period when most millers thought them out-dated and were replacing them with brick tower mills. Wetwang mill was different to most other post-mills in another respect, in being fitted with an unusual feature not found on many post-mills. In most cases the striking rod mechanism on the sails of the East Riding post-mills employed to open and close the shutters, was controlled by a rack and pinion arrangement. Here, however, a rocking lever was fitted, and the windmill provided with a rear platform to give access to the striking chain. This arrangement is more commonly found on the later tower mills of the nineteenth century, which shows that while the miller was perhaps old-fashioned in some ways, he was nevertheless familiar with current trends in windmill design to install the latest type of gearing to his windmill when available.

The old post-mill at Wetwang, mounted on a *'roundhouse'* for storage. (From the author's collection)

Whitby, Anderson's Mill (NY)

Variously known as *Anderson's Mill*, *Arundel Mill*, or *Fletcher's Mill*, was the windmill at Stakesby, now a suburb of Whitby. Mentioned in a conveyance document of October 1778, it was described as a *Wind Corn Mill* in the ownership of Elizabeth Knaggs and James Lewis, and was probably the same corn mill referred to in a later mortgage release dated 28 May 1798. In another conveyance dated 4 August 1863 a windmill and site at Stakesby is again mentioned. The miller given as George Fletcher.

In an advertisement in the *Whitby Gazette* of 27 March 1869, a windmill was *for let, and may be entered upon the 13th day of May next, the WIND MILL at Stakesby, near Whitby, together with the HOUSE, and GRANARIES; also a GRASS FIELD, and a large GARDEN. For rent and particulars apply to Mr William Ruff, Stakesby, Whitby.*

The corn mill at Lower Stakesby, which the Whitby local historian the Reverend George Young mentions in 1817, was in his time in the occupation of Thomas Anderson. At some time it had been an oil-mill. It was pulled down in 1877. The site of the mill formed part of the garden of a house named *Arundel Howe* erected by Edward Swales in that year. As a consequence of this, there may have been more than one windmill at Stakesby. In a conveyance dated 20 June 1898, *a messuage and Dwelling House, Wind Corn Mill, Granaries, Close [called] … Wind Mill Field … situated at or near Lower Stakesby*, clearly cannot have been the one demolished in 1877 unless it had been replaced.

Anderson's Mill at Stakesby is illustrated in Gaskin's, *The Old Seaport of Whitby* (1909) and can be seen as a circular tower mill standing three storeys high and having, unusually, a tiled ridge roof. It also shows the endless chain arrangement at the rear by which the miller could operate the rocking lever mechanism that adjusts the shutters on the four patent sails.

Union Mill, Whitby, photographed by Frank Meadow Sutcliffe in the 19th century.

Whitby, Union Mill (NY)

The foundation stone of the *Whitby Union Mill* was laid on the 16 June 1800, and on a pottery mug produced to commemorate the event an inscription runs, *From Stormy Blasts and Dangers ill May God Protect the Union Mill*. This sentiment served well for eighty years until 1880, when a storm damaged the windmill almost beyond repair.

Formed as the Union Mill Industrial and Provident Society Limited, the Reverend Young wrote, *"it was set on foot by liberal benefactions, including a legacy of £100 left by Mrs Hancock, yet it is more properly a trading company than a charity; each of its members, whose number amounts to about 900, enjoying a share in the profits of the concern, by obtaining flour at a reduced price. The windmill and premises belonging to this society form a conspicuous object on the west side of Whitby. For 14 years, the business was conducted by Mr John Watson, president, and a committee annually renewed … At the beginning of 1815, a revolution took place in the society, attended with circumstances over which the historian would wish to throw a veil. Suffice it to remark, that the treatment which Mr Watson and others received after long, arduous, and disinterested labours, illustrates a well known truth that he who serves the public, must serve it from a sense of duty, rather than from a hope of*

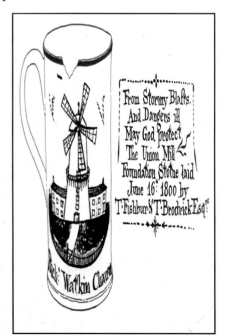

A Member's ticket showing the square stamp marks around the upper edge.

gratitude. In both its periods, the mill seems to have answered its principal design, of furnishing good and cheap flour for the use of a great part of the inhabitants of Whitby".

A footnote goes on to state, *"The society has been very unfortunate in its rules, the original rules being in some part defective, and liable to abuse, while those now acted upon are partly tyrannical and partly puerile".*

Notices of a share out were given periodically among various sources including the *Whitby Gazette.*

Union Mill Industrial & Provident Society Ltd
On Tuesday, February 14th, the Committee will attend at the Mill from Nine o'clock in the morning until Four o'clock in the Afternoon, to deliver to each Member A STONE OF BEST FLOUR, on producing their Ticket. One penny per stone will be charged to pay Meal Sellers for their attendance, and for defraying the incidental expenses. Members omitting to attend on the above mentioned day, may receive their flour on the Wednesday, Thursday, or Friday, following, by applying to the President with their Tickets, and paying sixpence extra for each stone. It is required by the Committee that every Ticket be registered in the name of the present owner; and it is requested, that any persons intending to purchase a Ticket, should previously ascertain from the President, if it is properly registered.
Whitby, February 3rd, 1860
R HORNE, PRESIDENT

An example of a share-holder's ticket displays a remarkable facet of English folk-lore worth mentioning. Inspection of the ticket reveals curious little punch marks, square-shaped, around the upper edge. These denote how many times it was used and led to the saying *having been through the mill.* (Illustration on p.70)

Union Mill was a large, five-sailed windmill mounted on a three-storey building. On 5 October 1880 a fierce storm damaged the sails and partially blew the roof off. The society repaired and continued for some years until on 11 July 1888 the Union Mill Society was wound up. Soon after the windmill and buildings were sold. By 1912, the mill premises had been converted into stables and armoury by the Territorial Army Association, and it continued as such until it was demolished.

An extremely prominent landmark in the town, it stood on a site now partly occupied by Harrison's Garage at the top of Chubb Hill and was photographed a number of times by the eminent nineteenth century local photographer, Frank Meadow Sutcliffe.

A mug produced to commemorate the founding of Whitby Union Mill.

Whitby, Wren's Mill (NY)

On a map published by Wood dated 1828, three windmills are shown in Whitby, one of which on a later Ordnance Survey map is called *Bagdale Windmill (Corn).*

It is possible that this mill at Bagdale may have come into existence in the eighteenth century. Like the mill at Stakesby, *Bagdale Mill* was known by various titles throughout its life, named after successive owners *Burnett's Mill*, *Noble's Mill*, and *Wren's Mill*. Demolished in 1862, it was last in the ownership of a Mr Chapman, with George Burnett the final tenant. He is mentioned in a conveyance dated 17 April 1857 which reads in part, *all that Wind Corn Mill and messuage cottage or dwelling-house situated in or near Bagdale … now in the occupation of George Burnett and also two closes in or near Bagdale called Bagdale Mill Field containing 6a 1r 11p and Bagdale Far Field containing 7a 2r 10p.* Burnett had the mill for about eighty years until it closed down in 1861.

Illustrated in Gaskin, it appears as a small circular windmill with perp-endicular sides, unlike the majority of mills that usually taper. It also has a depressed ogee-shaped cap. It is shown as having four sails, yet in a print published in 1842 by J F Howard which shows clearly the three mills of Whitby, *Wren's Mill*, seen in the foreground, has six sails.

The site of *Wren's Mill* was beside *the west side of the North eastern Railway, between Whitby Town and West Cliff stations, opposite the back of the Roman Catholic convent since erected near Chubb Hill Road* an area known as ***Mill Factory Field***. A more detailed description of the mill site and final fate states, *to the left of the path up Stakesby Fields, after crossing the North Eastern Railway bridge, are some piggeries and cowhouses in a field in the occupation of Mr Walshaw. These are partially built of old material of the mill. The mill stood in direct line between these piggeries and the railway line (6yds to piggeries, 10yds to railway line). There was just sufficient room for the mill wings to revolve between the mill building and the piggeries.*

Wilberfoss Mill in 1935, still complete and in good order.

Wilberfoss (EY)

At Wilberfoss, a windmill was included in the grant of the former Priory property there to George Gale in 1533. A windmill was mentioned again in 1624 and may have been the same as that recorded in 1669. A second mill stood at Wilberfoss from 1823, and a miller was last recorded in operation in 1933, the same year that Karl Wood made a painting of a windmill that shows it already disused and with only partial sails. This windmill was sited on a moraine north-east of Wilberfoss. The name *Mill Field* on early maps suggests that there was at least one earlier windmill in the parish and in 1755 an oat-meal mill stood near the beck at Wilberfoss, close to the stone bridge.

A windmill at Wilberfoss is remembered by Marjorie Williams, whose great uncle came as miller to the village in the nineteenth century. She recalls in the *Dalesman* how the windmill — a wooden post-mill — *sat on the hill top above the village on a ridge stretching towards Stamford Bridge* and how local farmers, including the millers, *used to tell of turning up pieces of rusty metal which they believed to have been parts of weapons used in the battle fought on the spot.*

Mrs Williams also recounts details of the mill's destruction on *Plow Monday* in the year 1838, when *John Rowntree and his brother, both bachelors who lived there,* farmed the land and worked the windmill.

During the day a mighty wind arose and darkness brought no lull in the storm. Through the howling of the gale the brothers could hear the groaning and the creaking of the wooden structure above them.

Throughout the years the timber had stood many a buffeting but this time the strain was too great and just after daybreak it fell with a great crash. Hastening to the door the two men saw their life's work a jumbled heap of beams and machinery before their eyes. The clattering sails on their mighty cross-arms would be heard no more and the village down in the valley had lost an essential part of everyday life.

The brothers after careful consideration, for there was no insurance to draw, decided to build a successor mill on site. Named Phoenix Mill — as it would rise from the ruins, and not be made of wood but something more lasting — brick.

John Rowntree went to his friend George Grey, the builder and put the proposition to him. Despite the fact that he had never undertaken such a job before, he agreed to do it. His workmen did a good job for a daily wage of half-a-crown and the windmill stood for over a century, a landmark for the whole district.

Yapham near Pocklington (EY)

Yapham Mill was built in 1805, by William Daniel, millwright, of Pocklington. Photographed in 1935 the cap and sails have gone, but the curb remains. The ground floor and the first floor are known to still retain some of the original machinery. Built of brick, the mill is *waisted*, and is not unlike Holgate windmill in York. Such a design is typical of Lincolnshire windmills.

Roy Gregory in *East Yorkshire Windmills* records the 'stone floor', set at first floor level, at some time contained three pairs of stones, two pairs of French Burrs four feet in diameter and one pair of Peak stones measuring 4 feet 2 inches in diameter. There is no maker's name around the eye of one of the French stones and the runner stone has disappeared from the other pair. However, a piece of broken casting possibly from the missing runner stone suggests that they were from one of the Hull firms of French stone maker's. Originally, it is thought that when first erected, the mill had only two pairs of stones.

Yapham Mill in 1935.

York, Burton Stone Lane (NY)

Burton Stone Lane was for centuries nothing more than a country lane, until it began to be developed as a suburban residential area about 1850. Toward the end of the fourteenth century there stood at its northern end a windmill, which is described in a record dated 1374 as *the mill of John de Roucliffe*. In those times it bore the name of *Lady Mill*. John de Roucliffe was the founder in 1373 of a hospital in Fossgate dedicated to the *Blessed Mary the Virgin and the Holy Trinity*. This hospital throughout its existence was associated with the York Merchant Adventurers. It seems probable that there was some connection between the name of the windmill and the dedication of the Fossgate hospital to *Our Lady*, but this is not confirmed in any documentation.

The site of the windmill was close to the side of the lane on the left, between the present Surtees Street and Garth

Burton Stone Lane Mill in May 1870, photographed by George Fowler Jones.

Terrace. The historian Davies indicates that a windmill stood here in his day and had the name of *Burton Mill*, and was one of two windmills hereabouts demolished around 1878, one of which was a post-mill.

This post-mill in the medieval period stood at a little distance beyond the entrance to Burton Stone Lane on the left side of the street to Clifton, behind a building that houses the junior section of St Peter's School, where there is a slight eminence. This is the supposed site of the windmill that is spoken of in records of the city boundaries dated 1374 and 1445 as *the Abbot of St Mary's Mill*. Little is known about this windmill, except that it no doubt it belonged to St Mary's Abbey.

York, Heworth (NY)

By 1614 at least seven corn windmills stood on Heworth Moor, and on 2 May during the *Siege of York*, many of these were burnt down and destroyed by Cromwell's army. There were still at least three windmills on the Moor in 1734. One had been owned and leased out by the Corporation in the sixteenth century. A windmill was referred to in 1746 when W Farrar agreed to pay £7 for the materials of an old mill on Heworth Moor as *It should be pulled down, being very ruinous and situated near the highway to be a nuisance*.

A windmill stood at the junction of Glen Road and Harcourt Street in 1850, the miller then was John Asquith. Later this brick mill was converted to a house with the addition of another circular storey built on top to which were added battlements. The windmill was demolished about 1890.

This windmill at Heworth was recorded by the artist George Nicholson in 1827. It was shown in his drawing as a tower mill with a cap, common cloth sails and a long tail-pole projecting at the rear by which the miller could turn the sails into the wind. The cap shown is the more unusual boat-style, not normally associated with Yorkshire windmills.

Interestingly, the artist George Nicholson appears to be related to a long line of corn millers of York including one who was the last miller at *Heworth Mill*. A James Nicholson

'Mill near Heworth, April 30, 1827' by George Nicholson. York City Art Gallery.

(b.1791) lived in Dale Street, Bishophill, and his occupation is listed as miller. His son James, born in 1829 at Bishophill, lived at Rouse Mill Lane, Soothill in 1881 and was also a corn miller. James Nicholson, junior, had two sons Fred and Charles among his seven offspring, both of whom were corn millers. It was Charles, who during his fifty years as a miller, worked *Heworth Mill* before its closure. His son Ernest Nicholson was a miller at the Leeds Industrial Co-operative Flour Mill, in Marshall Street, Leeds. A brother of Charles, John Nicholson, was a corn miller at *Thornaby Mill*, on Teeside.

York, Heslington (NY)

Windmills existed at Heslington from an early date. Timber trees at *Acomb Grange* went to make a post, axle-tree and spars for *Heslington Mill* in 1539. This wooden post-mill was possibly the same as George Nicholson drew in 1826. Its location in the village is uncertain, but from the illustration it appears to be standing on a prominent mound away from houses. Notice, too, the cross-tree foundations are further raised off the earth on stone blocks to allow air to circulate all round and ensure the timber remains dry.

Karl Wood painted a windmill at Heslington in April 1933. Again its exact location is not known, but this is a tower mill without cap and sails and derelict. At what period the post-mills were replaced is unclear but the mill that survived appears to date from the nineteenth century. The tower mill had four sails and was said to be in working order until the end, which came shortly after Wood visited here.

A feature of the brick tower mill was that the window openings are not placed in a vertical line above each other, but deliberately staggered. Some millwrights believed that to set openings in a straight line would cause a point of weakness and may possibly result in the tower splitting.

'Mill between Heslington and York, February 7, 1826' by George Nicholson. York City Art Gallery.

York, Holgate Mill (NY)

Of all the numerous windmills that have ever stood in York, the only one to survive is that at Holgate. At one time known as *Severus Mill*, its site can be traced back to 1366, when a post-mill first stood here. It is not known why it was called *Severus Mill* or when this name was changed.

The first miller of whom we have any record connected with *Holgate Mill*, was named William Plewman, who in 1573 was fined 13s 4d by the manor court *for not bringing the Toll Dishe according to custom*, a necessary duty attendant with the responsibility of medieval Soke Law. Other millers were Lancelot Scadlock (1597); a second William Plewman

Holgate Mill in 1935 after it had been closed. The sails are partially removed and the mill house has been demolished.

Holgate Mill in 1927, showing that it was still in operation at this time.

(1619); Edward Brittaine or Britton (1623); William Collier (1735) and George Waud or Ward (1770).

In 1792, it is recorded that George Ward had *latterly erected a brick windmill and adjoining dwelling house* replacing the earlier wooden post-mill with its single pair of stones and common cloth sails. It is this brick windmill of George Ward that stands today *on a Commanding Eminence at Holdgate, within a mile of the City of York. Holgate Mill* as it became known, remained in production until about 1930 when it closed due to its unsafe condition. The sails were removed at that time following storm damage, and attempts at restoration from then on by the York Corporation, resulted in a new cap being fitted in 1939.

The windmill is built to a design known as the *Lincolnshire Pattern* and incorporates a pronounced waist. Constructed of handmade brick and then tarred, it had an ogee-shaped cap similar to that of today, which then supported automatic fan-tail gearing to enable the top and sails to be turned into the wind.

When first built, the mill was fitted with *Hooper's Patent Roller Reefing Sails* that comprised of short lengths of canvas fitted to individual rollers, instead of rigid shutters. Unusually, it was powered by five sails. Later, Hooper's sails were replaced by patent double shutter sails, first introduced in 1807.

They had sail frames attached to both the trailing and leading edges of the sail backs and were fitted with shutters that operated like a Venetian Blind. These shutters were joined with a bar on each sail. All five bars were then connected to the *spider* in the centre of the assembly. This spider was activated by the striking rod that passed right through the centre of the hollowed wind-shaft to emerge at the tail of the windmill. Here, a chain wheel was mounted, over which hung an endless chain reaching down to the ground. It was on this chain that the miller hung weights to compensate for the force of the wind and so regulate the degree to which the shutters would open and in turn control the speed of the sails. To open the shutters was to *spill the wind* — to close them was *to catch the wind*.

The last corn miller at *Holgate Mill* was Thomas Mollet.

Today the mill remains almost complete though hemmed in by housing. Yet with such affection is Holgate windmill held, as, indeed, generally all windmill ruins are, that the Holgate Windmill Preservation Society was formed in 2001 to rescue and restore this magnificent giant. Enquiries to Brian Lambert on 01904 799295 or Richard Green on 01904 797165.

BRIEF GLOSSARY
OF TECHNICAL TERMS

Note: words in italics within an entry denote that a separate entry exists for these terms.

Air Brakes: longitudinal boards on the outer end of the leading edge of *sail*, operated by a shutter mechanism to slow the sail when in operation.

Back Stays: supporting bars across the rear of a windmill sail.

'Backwinded': term denoting the sails are not facing into the wind. In heavy wind such a situation can be dangerous and cause substantial damage to the sails.

Bar: lateral member of a sail frame.

Bedstone: the bottom half of a pair of *millstones* which remains stationary.

Bell Crank Lever: part of the *spider* that links the *striking rod* to the *uplongs*.

Body: of a *post-mill*, in which the machinery is sited, sometimes called the *buck*.

Brake: made of wood or iron. That part of the shoe which encircles the *brake wheel*.

Brake Wheel: cog wheel that runs around the rim on which the brake contracts to stop the windmill.

Brayer Lever: *lever beam* on which the *bridge tree* rests.

Breast: the lower part of the front of the *buck* of a *post-mill* just behind the *sails* that protects the *trestle* from the weather.

Breast Beam: main lateral beam of the breast taking the weight of the *wind-shaft*.

Bridge: metal bar cemented into the *eye* of *runner stone* to act as a bearing for the top of *spindle*.

Bridge Tree: *lever beam* which carries the lower end of *spindle* and so bears weight of *runner stone*.

Buck: the entire body of a *post-mill* above the *trestle* that revolves as the mill is *winded*.

Canister: large cast-iron double socket on the end of the *wind-shaft* through which the *stocks* of the sails pass.

Cant Posts: main corner beams of sections of a *smock mill*.

Cap: moveable top section of a *smock-* or *tower-mill*.

Cap Circle: lower bearing surface of *cap* that rests on the wall curb.

Centering Wheels: attached to cap frame and maintain position of *cap* in relation to tower.

Chain Wheel: turned by means of an endless chain and used in the operation of *winding* mill or for working the *striking gear*.

Cloth Sails: also known as common sails, constructed of a wooden frame covered by cloth which is tied onto the framework.

Composite Mill: a post-mill body taken off its post and mounted on a short tower.

Constant Pitch Sails: sails with rigid bars set at identical angles to the *whip* from inner to outer ends.

'Cracking': term relating to the cutting of fine grooves along the surface of a *millstone*, which usually form patterns known as drills, feathering or stitching.

Cross: multi-armed casting mounted on the end of the *wind-shaft* to carry the *sails* on its arms.

Cross Tree: main horizontal beams of the substructure of a post-mill that form the foundations of a *post-mill* from which the *main post* rises; also known as cross beams.

Crotch: Y-shaped attachment to the *quant* which slides over the bridge into the *mace* on over-driven *millstones*.

Crown Tree: main beam across the body of the *buck* on which pivots the top of the post in a *post-mill*.

Curb: track on top of a *tower mill* on which the *cap* revolves.

Double Shuttered: sail with *shutters* on both leading and trailing sides of the *whip*.

Dressing: (of stones) general term to mean sharpening.

Fan Stage: wooden supports and plat-form of the fan mechanism at the top of a *tower-* or *smock-mill*.

Fantail: often simply known as a **Fan**, small secondary wind propelled structure that automatically turns the *cap* to face into the wind.

Fantail Carriage: mounted on wheels and running on the ground, it is attached to the *tail-pole* and is used to turn the body of a *post-mill* into the wind.

Fly Tackle: another name for a *fantail*.

Fork Iron: part of a *spider* mechanism that joins levers to the *shutter bars* on a *sail*.

French Burrs: From France, considered the finest type of millstones. The *millstone* is made up of small blocks of extremely hard freshwater quartz, which is fitted together and bound with an iron ring.

Furrow/Furrow Strips: the low part of a pattern on the surface of a *mill-stone*.

Gallery: platform around the *cap* of a *tower mill*.

Great Spur Wheel: mounted on the upright shaft, it drives the *millstones* and other subsidiary machinery.

Grey Stones: *millstones* of millstone grit, sometimes called Peak Stones.

Grist: (*a*) corn to be ground (*b*) animal feed; hence the phrase *'grist to the mill'*.

Head: upper front part of a *post-mill*.

Heel: inner end of a windmill *sail*.

Hemlaths: pieces of wood running longitudinally along the edges of *sails* to hold the *bars* in place.

Jib Sail: triangular sail cloths wound round a radial sail arm with the tip of the sail corded to the next sail. Much favoured overseas.

Keep Irons: fitted to the *cap* to hold it down to the tower should the mill be *backwinded*.

Lands: high parts of the pattern on the surface of *millstones*.

Leader Boards: longitudinal boards on the front or leading edge of a *sail*.

Mace: jaws at the top of the spindle which slot over the *bridge* to provide the drive to the *runner stone*.

Main Post: upright post on which a *post-mill* revolves.

Main Shaft: vertical shaft from the *wallower* to spur wheel.

Mill Soke: manorial law governing the ownership, building and use of mills.

Millstones: term given to a pair of stones that grind the corn or millet.

Ogee Cap: type of domed cap with a reverse curve finishing in a pointed profile.

Patent Sails: shuttered sails linked through a *spider* to an automatic opening and closing mechanism. Invented in 1807 by Sir William Cubitt they became the most common form of sail.

Pepper Pot: type of *cap* with a high dome finished with a flat top instead of a finial.

Petticoat: vertical boarding on a *cap* to protect junction of same with tower against the weather.

Piers: of brick or stone, support the ends of the *cross trees* of a *post-mill* raising it above the ground.

Poll End: large cast-iron socket on the end of a *wind-shaft* through which the *stocks* pass.

Post: upright timber on top of which the body of a *post-mill* turns.

Post Mill: type of early windmill with a wooden body or *buck* that can revolve on the vertical *main post*, supported by a *trestle*.

Quant: four-sided shaft from stone nut to *mace*.

Quarter: a name given to one side of a *smock mill*.

Quarter Bars: diagonal beams from the outer ends of *cross trees* that support the *main post* below the *buck*.

Reef: a term relating to the method of reducing the working surface of a *common* or *cloth sail* by rolling up the material and securing it to the sail frame.

Rocking Lever Bar: for controlling the striking gear.

Roller Reef Sails: use roller blinds instead of shutters and are manually operated.

Roundhouse: (*a*) the walled and roofed *trestle* part of a *post-mill* providing dry storage space (*b*) of a tower mill, an additional roofed area built around the outside of the lower floor or floors.

Runner Stone: the top stone of a pair of *millstones* that turns.

Sails: also known as *sweeps* or *wands*. These are turned by the force of the wind to drive the main shaft.

Sail Backs: see *whips*.

Sail Bars: attached to the *whips* to carry *cloth sails* or *shutters*.

Sail Stocks: beams passing through the *canister* to carry the *whips*.

Shutter Bar: this links spring-loaded *shutters*.

Shutters: moveable vanes or springs of *patent sails* that open and close to reduce the working surface and so speed up or slow down sail movement.

Smock Mill: wooden-framed, multi-sided static windmill clad with wood or thatch with a moveable *cap*.

Spider: iron cross on the end of *striking rod*, linked to *bell cranks* and levers of *striking gear*.

'Spill the wind': term used to mean open the *shutters* in a sail that is turning.

Spring Sail: sail with shutters linked to a spring, the tension of which can be controlled manually so that the *shutters* will open and close according to wind strength.

Spring-Patent Sails: *patent sails* with springs incorporated into the *striking gear*.

Stocks: long bars that cross through the top of the *wind-shaft* and carry the *whips*.

Striking Gear: collective name for the mechanism front and rear, used to open and close (*a*) the *shutters* in a *patent sail* (*b*) the blinds of a *roller reefing sail*.

Striking Rod: passes through the *wind-shaft* and connects the front and rear *striking gear* in *patent* or *roller reefing sails*.

Sweeps: a localized name for sails (Kent).

Tail: rear end of a post-mill.

Tail Pole: long beam attached to the rear of a *post-mill* by which the body can be turned into the wind.

Tower Mill: static windmill built of brick or stone with a moveable cap.

Trestle: the name for the entire support system of a post-mill comprising the *cross trees*, *quarter bars*, *main post*, etc. that hold up the *buck*.

Turret Mill: composite windmill with a round brick base carrying a curb on which the *buck* rests.

Uplong: longitudinal bar in a *sail*.

Upright Shaft: on which the *wallower* and *great spur wheel* are mounted.

Vanes: the name for the sail part of a *fantail* or *shutters* of *patent sails*.

Wand: another name for the *sails* of a windmill.

Wallower: mounted at the top of the *main shaft* and meshing with the *brake wheel*; it is the first driven wheel of a windmill.

Whips: long bars attached to the front of the *stock* that carry the *sail bars*, *shutters* etc.

Winding: turning the mil so that the *sails* face square into the wind.

Wind-shaft: carries the *sails* and the *brake wheel*.

Gazetteer of Documented Yorkshire Corn Windmill Sites
[with earliest date where known]

Note : Entries in bold type denote windmill still in existence, the state of which is given if known. Ordnance Survey map reference given if available.

Aberford, Hicklam Mill (WY) [SE 434359] Converted to house.
Aberford, North Mill (WY) 18c
Acaster Malbis (NY) 1772
Acklam (EY) 1602
Ackworth (WY) 1420/21
Acomb (NY)
Adlingfleet (EY) 1590
Adwick-le-Street (NY) 1564 : 1841
Adwick supra Stratham (NY) 1564
Ainderby Steeple (NY) 1346
Aldborough (NY) 1549
Aldbrough (EY) 1772
Allerthorpe (EY) 1327
Allerton Mauleverer (NY) 1578
Alne (NY) 1611/12
Anlaby (EY) 1657
Appleton (NY) 1565
Appleton-le-Moors (NY) 1266
Appleton Roebuck (NY) [SE544425] Substantial derelict shell.
Argram (EY) 1557
Arkendale (NY) 14c
Armthorpe (SY) 1586
Armyn (EY) 1772
Arras (NY) 1554
Askern (SY) 1580
Askham Bryan (NY) [SE 543473] Converted to water tower.
Askham Richard (NY) 18c/19c
Asselby (EY) 1772
Aston-cum-Aughton (WY) 1834
Atwick (EY) 1582
Aughton (EY) 1603/4
Austerthorpe (WY) 19c
Ayton (NY) 1590
Azerley (NY) 1558

Babthorpe (EY) 1556

Bainton (EY) [SE 963527] Derelict stump.
Balne (NY) 1592
Barkisland (WY) 1566
Barlby (NY) 1553
Barley Gate [Beverley] (EY) 1578
Barmby Marsh (EY) 1295
Barnby-on-Don (SY) 1605
Barnsley (SY) 1822
Barton (NY) 1563
Barwick-in-Elmet (NY) 19c
Batley (WY) 16c
Beeford (EY) [TA 131535] Shell used as farm store.
Bempton (EY) [TA 180715] Converted to office/house.
Beningbrough (NY) 13c
Benningholme (EY) 1568
Bessacarr (SY) 1608
Bessinby (EY) 1608
Beverley (EY) 1551
    Beverley Parks c.1820
    Black Mill [TA 021390] Preserved shell.
    Crathorne Mill 19c
    Catterson Mill
    Far Mill 1706
    Fishwick Mill 1761
    Hither Mill c.1620
    Lowson Mill [TA 027386] Converted to a house.
    Union Mill [TA 022385] Part of Golf Club Premises.
    Westwood Mill 1625
Bielby (EY) 1566
Billbrough (WY) 1608
Bilton (EY) 1548
Birdsall (EY)
Birstall (WY) [SE 2226] Derelict stump.
Bishop Burton (EY) [SE 993392] Converted to a house.
Bishop Wilton (EY) [SE 790505] Derelict stump.
Bolton (Nr Bfd) (WY) 1772

Bolton Percy (NY) 1557
Boroughbridge (NY) [SE 376695] Substantial derelict shell.
Boynton (EY) 1352
Boythorpe (EY) 1616
Bramham (NY) [SE 432434] Converted to a water tower.
Brandsburton (EY) 1592
Branton (SY) [SE 633018] Derelict stump.
Brayton (EY) 1772
Brearley (WY) 1574
Bridlington (EY) 16c
    Anti/Spring Mill 1793
    Black Mill 1846
    Bridge Mill c.1500
    Colome Mill 1557
    Convent Mill 1557
    Duke/New Mill 1823
    Forty Foot Mill 1851
    Hilderthorpe Mill 16c
    Quay/Wetwam Mill 1793
    Quay/Folly Mill c.1825
    Spink Mill 1825
Brighouse (WY) 1566
Brierley (WY) 1772
Brodsworth (SY) 1604
Brookhouse (WY) 1772
Broomfleet (EY) 1287
Brompton (NY) 1612
Brotherton (WY) 1772
Bubwith (EY) 1772
Buckton (EY) 1341
Burn (WY) 1560
Burnby (EY) 1605
Burton Agnes (EY) 1265 : 1772
Burton Carr (EY)
Burton Fleming (EY) 13c
Burton Pidsea (EY) [TA 244309] Converted to a house.
Burstwick (EY) 13c
Butterthwaite/Scholes (SY) 1772
Butterwick (EY) 1359
Byram (NY) 1607

Campsall (SY) 1610
Cantley (SY) [SE 6202]

Substantial derelict shell.
Carleton (WY) 19c
Carlton (SY) 1772
Carnaby (EY) 1368
Catwick (EY) 1571
Cawood (NY) 1403
Cawthorne (SY) 1772
    Clough Green (SY)
Caythorpe (EY) 1296
Cayton (EY)
Chapel Haddlesey (SY) 1772
Cherry Burton (EY) [SE 9942] Used as farm store.
Church Fenton (NY) 1610
Clementhorpe [York] (NY) 1543
Cliffe (EY) 1477
Clifford [Nr Tadcaster] 18c
Clifton (WY) 1578
Clifton [Nr York] (NY) 1644
Coley [Nr Bradford] (WY) 1572
Colley (SY) 1588
Colton (NY) 1249
Colton Moor (NY) 19c
Conisborough (SY) 19c
Copmanthorpe (NY) 1609
Cornbrough (NY) 1569
Cottingham (EY) 1282
    North Mill c.1820
Cowick [2 mills] (WY) 1772
Cowlam (EY)
Cowthorpe (NY) 1572
Coxley (WY)
Cromwellbotham (WY) 1566
Crookes Broom (EY)
Croston (SY) 1580
Cundall-with-Leckby (NY) 1341

Danby Wiske (NY) 1285
Danthorpe (EY) 1608
Darrington (SY) [SE 4820] Converted to a house.
Deighton (EY) 1447
Dishforth (NY) 1420
Doncaster (SY) 1548
    Balby Road 1617
    Town Field 1822
Drax (NY) 1247

Drewton (EY) 1212
Driffield (EY)
    North End Mill 19c
Dringham (EY)
Dringhow (EY) 1585
Dromonby (NY) 17c
Dunnington (EY) c.1295
Dunsley [Nr Whitby] (NY) 1573

Earby (WY) 1583
Earswick (NY) 1608
Easington (EY) 1260
Easingwold (NY) 17c
Eastburn (EY) 1304
Eastburn (NY) 1572
Eastrington (EY) 1772
East Blacktoft (EY) 1576
East Cottingworth (EY) 1772
East Cowick (WY) [SE 666214]
    Derlict stump.
East Halsham (EY) 14c
Ecclesall (SY) 1645
Elland (WY) 1566
Elland Park (WY) 1566
Ellerby (NY) 1830
Ellerker (EY) 1822
Ellerton (EY) [SE 711399]
    Used as a farm store.
Elloughton (EY) 1540
Elmshall (SY) 1714
Elmswell (EY) 1597
Elstanwick (EY) 1772
Elstronwick (NY)
Elwick (NY) [NZ 43 SW]
    Derelict shell.
Escrick (NY) 1290
Eshton (NY) 1611
Etton (EY) [SE 981428]
    Derelict shell.
Everingham (EY) 1287
Everthorpe (EY) 1810

Farlington (NY) 1588
Ferriby (EY) 18c
Ferry Fryston (WY)
    Used to stable animals.
Filey (EY) 16c
Fimber (EY)
Firby (NY) 1566
Fishlake (EY) [SE 651132]
    Derelict shell.
    Nabbs Mill

North Mill
Fitling (EY)
Flamborough (EY) 1593 : 1772
Flawith (NY) 1772
Flixton (NY) 1225
Flockton/Emley (WY) 1772
Flotmanby (EY) 13c
Folkton (EY) 1246
Foston-on-Wolds (EY) [TA092548]
    Derelict stump.
Foxholes (EY) 1614
Fraisthorpe (EY) 1212
Frickley (WY) 1772
Fridaythorpe (EY) 1564
Frimarsh (EY) 14c
Fulford [Nr York] (NY) 1614
Fyling/Whitby (NY) 1551

Ganstead (EY) 1572 : 1772
Ganton (EY) 1585
Garton (EY) [TA 261358]
    Derelict shell.
Garton Slack (EY) 18c
Giggleswick (NY) 1611
Gilberdyke (EY) 1772
Gildersome (WY)
Glusburn (NY) 1572
Godmanham (EY) [SE 8843]
    Converted to a house.
Golcar (WY) 1566
Goldsborough (WY) 1571
Goole, Hook Road (EY) [SE 7524] Converted to a house.
    Heron Mill
    Timms Mill
Goole Fields (EY)
Gransmoor (EY)
Greasborough (SY) 1849
Greenhaigh (EY) 1581
Greetland (WY) 1566
Great Dromanby (NY) 1619
Great Houghton (SY) 1566
Great Ouseburn (NY) 1561
Grimston (EY) 1588
Grindale (EY) c.1295
Gristhorpe (NY) 1595
Guiseley (WY) 18c

Hagthorpe (EY) 1583
Haldenby (EY) 1622
Halsham (EY) 1294
Hambleton Haugh (WY) 1772

Harland Way (EY) 1772
Harthill (SY) 1591
Hatfield, Moss Croft Lane (SY)
    Converted to a house [SE 660083].
    Lings Mill 17c
Hatfield Woodhouse (SY) [SE 671089]
    Derelict shell.
Hawnby (NY) 1534
Hawsker (NY) 1557
Havercroft (WY) 1580
Haywold (EY) 19c
Headley [Nr Bfd] (WY) 1583
Heckmondwike (WY) 1772
Hedon (EY) 1575
Hellaby (SY) 19c
Helperthorpe (EY)
Hemingborough (EY) 18c
Hemingbrough (EY) 1276
Hemlington (NY) 1772
Hemsworth (WY) 1580
Hesley Wood (SY) 1567
Heslington (NY) 1530/1794
Hessle (EY) 1601
Higham Common (SY) 1747
High Belthorpe (EY)
High Egbrough (SY) 1772
Highfields (WY)
High Leven, North Mill (NY)
    South Mill
Hillam (WY)
Hinderwell (NY) 1374
    Royal George 19c
Hipperholme (WY) 1566
Hipswell (NY) 1563
Hollym (EY) 1226
Holme (EY)
Holme-on-Spalding Moor (EY) 1772
Holmpton (EY) 14c
Hook (SY) 1546
Hooten Pagnell (SY) 1772 : 1817
Horbury (WY) [SE 2918]
    Converted to a house.
Hornby (NY)
Hornsea (EY) [TA 197479]
    Converted to a house.
Howden (EY) 1566
    Hail's Mill [SE 754277]
        Derelict shell.
Huggate (EY) 1592

Hull, Eyres Mill (EY) [TA 123309]
    Preserved as *Mill Inn*.
    [7 mills +] 1349 [4] 1772
Hunmanby (EY) 1298 : 1772 [2]
Hunslet [Nr Leeds] (WY) 1425 : 1772
Hunsley (EY) 1324
Hutton Bonville (NY) 1565
Hutton Buscell (NY) 1590
Hutton Cranswick (EY) [TA 022531]
    Used as farm store.
Hunsworth (WY) 1566
Huntingdon (NY) 1322

Ingleby Barwick (NY) 18c

Keighley (WY) 1580 [4]
Kelfield (EY) 1569
Kellington (WY) [SE 546243]
    Converted to a house.
Kexby (EY)
Keyingham, Old Mill [TA 244526]
    Converted to a house.
    New Mill (EY) [TA 254251]
        Converted to a house.
    East/Lowther Mill 1811
    Eyres/Church Mill 1828
Kilham (EY) [TA 060641]
    Converted to a house.
Killamarsh [Nr Cawthorne] (WY) 18c
Killerby (NY) 1549
Killingbeck/Leeds (WY) 1772
Kilnsea (EY) 1260
Kilnsey (NY) 1571
Kilnwick (EY) 1571 [2]
Kilpin (EY)
Kimberworth, Grange Mill (SY) 1822
Kippax/Leeds (WY) [SE 427299]
    Used as a farm store.
Kirkby Hill (NY)
Kirkby Malham (NY)
Kirkbymoorside (NY) [SE 694863]
    Converted to a house.
Kirk Deighton (NY) 1562
Kirk Ella (NY) 1598 : 1772
Kirk Hammerton (NY) 1772
Kirk Leavington (NY) 1262
Kirklees (WY) 1539

Kirk Smeaton (WY) 17c
Knaresborough (NY) 1772
Knedington (EY) 1593
Knottingley (WY) 1772

Langacre (NY) 1572
Langtoft (EY) [TA 005680]
    Converted to a house.
Laughton-en-le-Morthen (SY) 1772
Laxton (NY) 1603
Leathley (WY) 1583
Leaven (EY) 1772
Leconfield (EY) 1314
Leeds, Sugar Mill (WY) [SE 3036] Converted to a house.
    Buslingthorpe
        Seacroft [SE 361356]
            Part of a Hotel.
    Wortley 1772
Lelley (EY) [TA 219326]
    Substantial derelict shell.
Lennerton (NY) 1558
Leven, New Mill (EY) [TA 117453] Derelict stump.
    Wrights Mill 1807
Little Smeaton 13c
Lockington (EY) 1558
Loftsholme (EY) c.1838
Long Preston (NY) 1611
Loversall (SY) 1608
Low Hawsker (NY) [NZ 925076]
    Used as a farm store.
Lund (EY) 1598
Lupset (WY) 1561

Malham-in-Craven (NY) 1553 [2]
Malton (NY) 1578
Mappleton (EY) [TA 224438]
    Substantial derelict shell.
Marfleet (EY) 1595
Market Weighton (EY)
Marton (EY) 1599 : 1772
Marston (NY) 1565
Masbrough (SY) 18c
Melbourne (EY) 1285
Middlestown (WY) [SE 2617]
    Converted to a house.
Middleton-on-the-Wolds (EY)
Mirfield (WY) 1566
Molescroft [Beverley] (EY) 1625
Monk Bretton (SY) 14c

Monk Fryston (SY)
Moor Monkton (NY) 1526
Morley (WY) 1772
Mulgrave/Whitby (NY) 19c
Muston [Nr Filey] (NY) [TA 107799]
    Substantial derelict shell.
Myton (EY) 1293 [2]

Naburn (NY) 1345 : 1772
Nafferton (EY) [TA 594128]
    Derelict shell.
Nether Hall (SY) 1772
Nether Sedbury (EY) 1562
Nether Sykes (SY) 1555
Newbiggin (NY) 1563
Newholm/Whitby (NY)
Newport (EY) 1795
Newsham (EY) 1441
Newton-on-Ouse (NY) 1815
Norland (WY) 1566
Normanby/Whitby (NY) 1772
Normanton (WY) 1394
North Anston (SY) 1772
North Burton (EY) 1772
North Cowton (NY) 1565 [6]
North Dalton (EY) 1623
North Ferrybridge (WY) 1604
North Frodingham (EY) 1610
North Milford (NY) 1612
Norton [Doncaster] (SY) [SE 537148] Converted to a house.
Nostell (WY) 1580
Nuthill (EY) 1301

Oakwell [Nr Batley] (WY) 1565
Octon (EY) 1323
Old Malton (NY) [SE 793740]
    Used as a farm store.
Osgodby (EY) 19c
Otteringham (NY) 1534
Ottringham (EY) 12c : 1772 [2]
    Carr Mill c.1815
Out Newton (EY) 1265
Ousefleet (EY) 1597
Ovenden (WY) 1566
Over Sedbury (EY) 1562
Overton (NY) 1598
Owstick (EY) 1568
Owthorne (EY) 1294 : 1772

Patrington (EY) 1340 [2]

East Mill 1426
Goodrick Mill [TA 321223]
    Used as a farm store.
Haven Mill [TA 309219]
    Used as a farm store.
South Mill 1810
West Mill 1544
Paull (EY) 17c
Pickering (NY) 19c
Pickhill (NY) 1614
Picton (NY) 1566
Pensthorpe (EY) 1349
Pocklington (NY)
Pollington (EY) 1772
Pontefract (WY) [SE 4521]
    Converted to a house.
    Dandy Mill c.1803
    St Thomas Mill 19c
Poppleton (NY) 1656
Preston (EY) 13c [2]
Portington (EY) 1594
Pudsey/Fulneck (WY) 1772

Ravenscar (NY) [NZ 976007]
    Substantial derelict shell.
Ravenser Odd (EY) 1260
Reedness (EY) [SE 7923]
    Converted to a house.
Reighton (EY) 1580
Renton (NY) 1772
Riccall (EY) [SE 617374]
    Now a restaurant.
Rievaulx Abbey (NY)
Rillington (NY)
Risby (EY) 17c
Rishworth (WY) 1566
Ross (EY) 1772
Rotherham, Doncaster Gate (SY) 19c [2]
Rothwell (WY) 1772
Routh (EY) 1549
Rowenstall (WY) 1566
Rudston (EY) 1296
Ryhill (WY) 14c : 1772
Ryston-in-Holderness (EY) 1538

Sancton (EY) 1538
Sandal [Nr Wakefield] (WY) 1270
Sand Hutton (NY)
Sawley (NY) 1585
Saxton-cum-Scarthingwell (NY) 1425

Scalby (EY) 1772
Scarborough (NY) [TA 036884]
    Now part of a hotel.
    Albion Mill 1860
    Common/Harrisons Mill 1852
    Falsgrave Mill 1275 : 1772
    Greengate Mill 1852
    South Cliff Mill 1523
Scarthingwell (NY) 1542
Scholey Hill (WY) 14c
Scorborough (EY) 1562
Scoreby (EY) 1339
Sculcoates/ Hull (EY) 1558
Seaton Ross, Fisher's Mill [SE 777421] Derelict shell.
    Preston's Mill [TA 774418]
        Derelict shell.
Sedburgh (NY) 1574
Selby (NY) 1579
Sewerby (EY) [TA 189713]
    Converted to an office.
Sewerby/Thirsk (NY) 1561
Shafton (SY) 1574
Sharleston (WY) 1772
Sheffield, Castle Mill (SY) 1602 [5]
Shelf (WY) 1566
Sheriff Hutton (NY) 1282
Shippen (WY) 14c
Skeckling (NY) 13c
Skeffling (EY) 1260
Skelder/Whitby (NY)
Skelton-on-Ure (NY) 1271
Skerne (EY) 1310
Skidby (EY) [TA 020333]
    Working Windmill Museum.
Skipsea (EY) 1372 : 1772
Skipwith (EY) 1320 [2] : 1772
Skipworth (EY) 1536
Skirlaugh (EY) 18c
Skircoat [Nr Halifax] (WY) 1566
Snaith (EY) 1608
Snape (NY) 18c
Sneaton/Whitby (NY)
Sniddall (WY) 1772
Soothill/Batley (WY) 1549
South Dalton (EY) c.1420
South Duffield (EY) 1300
South Kirby (WY)
Southowram (WY) 1566
Spaldrington (EY) 1772

Speeton (EY) 1772
Sproatley (EY) 1800
Stainforth (SY) 1579 : 1772
Stainland (WY) 1566
Stainsacre/Whitby (NY)
Stainton (NY) 1591
Stakesby/Whitby (NY)
Stamford Bridge, West Mill (NY) 1339
Stanghow (NY) 1304
Starbeck (NY)
Staxton (EY) c.1300
Steeton (NY) 1572
Stillingfleet (EY) 1244
Stittenham (NY) 1603
Stokesley (NY) 1378
Studley (NY) 1572
Stutton (NY) [SE 746421]
    Derelict shell.
Sutton (EY) 1565 : 1772
Sutton (NY) 1578
Sutton-on-Derwent (NY) 1567
Sutton-on-Hull (EY) 1640
Swanland/Hull (EY)
Swaythorpe (EY)
Swine (EY) 1568
Swinefleet (EY) 1618 : 1772
Swinton (EY) 1614
Swinton (WY) 17c
Swinton (SY) 1571
Sykehouse (EY) [SE 625174]
    Derelict shell.

Tadcaster (NY)
Tankersley (WY) 1591
Tarnston (NY) 1549
Terrington (NY) 1588
Tharlesthorpe (EY) 14c
Thearne (EY) 1625
Thorganby (EY) 1427 : 1772 [2]
Thorne (EY) 1772 [3]
Thorne (SY) [SE 686137]
    Derelict shell.

Cassons Mill
Crusts/Bellwood Mill 1629
Far Post Mill
Hemingways Mill
Oates Mill 19c
Oldfield Mill
Thorne/Alverthorpe (WY) 1275
Thorngumbald (EY) 14c
Thornhill (WY) 1566
Thornhill Edge (WY) 1772
Thornton (EY) 1577
Thornton-le-Clay (NY) [SE 677656]
    Derelict shell.
Thorpe (EY) 1584
Thorpe Audlin (WY) 1313
Thorpe Bassett (NY) c.1375
Thorpe Salvin, Peck Mill (SY) 1822
    Moor Mill 1822
Thrybergh (SY) 1841
Thurnscoe (SY) 1844
Thwing (EY)
Tickhill (SY) 1277
Tollerton (NY) [SE 514638]
    Converted to a house.
Towton, North Mill (NY)
    South Mill
Treeton (SY) 1822
Trumfleet (SY) 19c
Tunstall (NY) 1562
Tunstall (EY)
Tuntoft (EY)

Uffleet (EY) 1554
Ugthorpe (NY) [NZ 792116]
    Converted to holiday cottage.
Ulleskelf (NY) [SE 390519]
    Converted to a house.
Upton (WY) 1580
Upton Beacon (WY)

Waddermarsh (SY) 1571
Waddington (WY) 1563
Wadsworth (WY) 1566
Wakefield (WY) 1270
Walkington (EY) 1772
Walton (WY) 1554
Warmfield-cum-Heath (WY) 1461
Warthermaske (NY) 1571
Wath-upon-Dearne (SY)
Waxholme (EY) [TA 326292]
    Derelict stump.
Weedley (EY) 1185
Weel (EY) c.1600
Welham (NY) 1599
Weirway (EY)
Well (NY) 18c
Welwick (EY) 1611
Wentworth/Barrow [SK 378986]
    Converted to a house.
    Roundhouse 1745
West Cottingworth (EY) 1688
West Garforth (WY) 1567
West Harsley (NY) 1540
West Hardwick (WY) 1580
West Hatfield (EY) 1608 [2]
West Lutton (EY) 1533
Wetwang (EY) 18c
Wheatley/Doncaster (SY) c.1322
Wheldrake (EY) 1719
Whitby (NY) 14c
    Andersons Mill c.1769
    Bagdale/Wrens Mill 18c
    Union Mill 1800
Whitgift (EY) 1597 : 1772
Whixley (NY) 14c
Whorlton (NY) 1614
Wibsey/Bradford (WY) 1772
Wickersley (SY) 1822
Wiggington (NY) 1540 : 1772
Wighill (NY) 1585 [2]
Wilberfoss (EY) 1553

Willerby (EY) 17c
Winestead (EY) 1489 : 1636 [2]
Wintersett/Wakefield (WY) 1580
Wistow (NY) 1592
Withernick (EY) 1304 : 1772
Wold Newton (EY) 1819
Wombwell, Aldham Mill (SY) 18c
Woodhall (NY) 1580
Woolley (WY) 14c
Worsall (NY) 1587
Worsborough Dale (SY) 1624
Wrenthorpe (WY) 1580
Wressle (EY) [SE 710312]
    Used as a farm store.

Yapham (EY) [SE 790505]
    Derelict shell.
Yokefleet (EY) [SE 821237]
    Used as an animal shelter.
York, Bootham Stray (NY)
    Burton Stone/Lady Mill 1374 [2]
    Dalton Terrace
    Fishergate
    Heworth Moor 1644 [7] 1772 [5]
    Holgate [SE 584517]
        Preserved shell with cap.
    Lamel Hill
    Lunn
    Millfield, Hull Road
    Mill Mount
    Monk Stray
    Parish, Bishophill, Jnr 1620
    Parish, Holy Trinity 1580
    Parish, Holy Trinity (Micklegate)
    Parish, St Belfrid 1590
    Parish, St Edward 17c
    Parish, St Lawrence 1618 [2]
    Parish, St Nicholas
    Vyner Street c.1620
    White House Mill